HIGH HEELS

&

DIRTY DEALS

HIGH HEELS

&

DIRTY DEALS

Globetrotting Tales of Debauchery
from a Binge-Drinking Nymphomaniac

BRETT TATE

Brett Tate's latest controversial release…
from the author of the bestseller:

The Professional Bachelor: How to Exploit her Inner Psycho
(ISBN – 09752640-2-8)
and his Ultimate Bachelor's Vacation Guide:
The Hedonist
(ISBN – 09752640-0-1)

Published by: Cambridge Publishing, LLC

ISBN 0-9752640-4-4
ISBN 978-0-9752640-4-1   Printed in the United States

"In a relentless pursuit of seducing exotic women and the allure of fast money, I've traveled the far corners of the globe, taking absurd risks with investments and my life, overindulged in every vice, bedded an embarrassingly large number of women, and savored the bounty from stimulating to obscene. For a decade I've authored "Tales from the Trenches" for a select few friends; penning and photographing the raw, the hilarious, and the erotic to psychotic adventures. After years of provocation, and perhaps against my better judgment, they've convinced me that before I'm in prison or dead, I need to share some of my life's tales as a gambler, an adrenaline junkie and a binge-drinking nymphomaniac, for the world to peer at in awe, envy, or disgust.

The following is a true documentary of a typical four day trip of mayhem and debauchery from a few years back. Seeing as there are dirty bankers, gangsters, brothels, drugs, guns, and few laws or morals respected, the participants' names and conspicuous details have been changed to avoid an early dirt nap. Nostrovia."

Contents

Day One

The Hunt for Ms. Red Crotchtober	1
Nuking the Eurotrash Café	8
Moscow – A Dangerous and Intoxicating Beast	17
Deep Oral Highway during a Police Chase	20
Bootie and the Beast do the Walk of Shame	28
For Your Thighs Only	33
Good Evening Mr. Bond	43
Alchoholocaust at the Bely Medved Brothel	51

Day Two

Trolling for Gen-X Nymphos - starring Ivana Suckit	77
The Navy Seal Coochie Bandit	94
Gangster Styling in the Ultimate Crib	100
Bisexual Orgy in a McDonald's Drive-thru	115
Sodom and Gomorrah Orgy	121
Old School Meets the Beast from the East	125
Armed and Hammered at Nightflight	129
National Pornographic	156

Day Three

The Calm before the Storm	168
The Mouth – the Return of Ivana Suckit	169
Pocahotass and the MILF DILF BJ Contest	180
Special Olympics Drunk at the Den of Sin	196

Day Four

Sledgehammer Hangover	218
Hunting Private Lolitas – Road trip into the Provinces	220
Schoolgirl Threesome in Public	227
The Old Coot finds his Mojo	240

1.
THE HUNT FOR
Ms. RED-CROTCHTOBER

M y eyes lock on her . . .

Mysterious and demure, a tight little spinner appears on the horizon, poured into a stylish coral blue miniskirt below a teal silk blouse. She's a scorching Ukrainian hottie of sleek Grade-A beef, in a hurry to go nowhere in particular. With gorgeous long braided hair exposing diamond earrings, she wears a snazzy hat, a white south sea pearl necklace and Royal Blue Bvlgari scarf resting on delicate shoulders. She drips with a sensual class.

Peering into the lazy pastel sky with watery green eyes and swollen pouty lips, she hums her life's song of gentle desires, with a pulsating bass line throbbing with pain. The vanishing sunset gives final life to her vivid colors, and at the right angle, shines clear through the near transparent miniskirt, exposing a crimson red lace thong. *Bozhe moi.* Camel toe Paradise. Yummy.

Sprawled out on the sidewalk, the street bum voyeurs heartily approve of their view, while passionately clutching the Ted Kennedy binge-drinking driver's manual; *"How to crash into city traffic going 110mph, blow a .35 BAC and get off."*

With dripping chins and toothless grins, they toast their good fortune and slam an obscenely large moonshine chug, while farting their life's song *Zip-a-dee-doo-dah* out the ass.

My eyes zoom in on her . . .

Her walk is tall and hypnotic, though she seeks no attention strolling down Moscow's cosmopolitan Tverskaya Avenue. Deliciously elegant. Sensually lethal. Fresh enough to be a sophomore at the School of Hard Knockers. It's a mesmerizing view as she gracefully struts away with her gazelle legs above perilous stilettos, snapping her heart-shaped bubblebutt.

For visiting businessmen and tourists, such exquisiteness and pure breeding makes merely breathing a challenge. It turns your hormones upside down and rips your heart inside out. No virile man can honestly claim immunity to its power.

\-   -   -

The Johnson moves to the right side of the zipper, a trained hound dog catching the scent of rabbit. Brett, the master of coochie challenges, moves straight into sexual predator mode. A healthy hour of power-drinking awakens the gluttonous hunter, like gladiator to shiny sword. The horns rise. The crotch swells.

The eye's red laser dot travels down her drooping neckline. Her tantalizing fun bags beckon me to stick my head between them, licking and slobbering while singing 14th century pirate songs. Without thought, Brett locks and loads his seduction phasers and plots his ground offensive, while picturing her handcuffed butt naked to a Molson keg in his billiard room.

With an insatiable ego and hardcore bartender feeding it at a vicious pace, the Johnson easily convinces me her destiny is to drop down on her knees and service me.

My eyes scope her . . .

for conflicting evidence. A swift gust of wind tosses her hat to the pavement, the edge of her chic bonnet landing in a puddle of inhumane industrial waste and urine. She scoops it up, cursing violent nothings under her breath. But as she bends over, for one scant instant, the clues peek out; a tiny barbwire tattoo on her shoulder, a tramp stamp, and a studded black leather ankle bracelet.

"I see you...," The Johnson whispers, a bonafide Whorehunter in his own right. As suspected, this *dyev* has an alternative life story, the telltale signs she is game.

My eyes undress her . . .

Brett breathes with feverish anticipation, being a dirty old man since the ripe age of thirty. My steps in the shadows quicken for positioning. In a few stolen moments, I study her style and personality; a fine-tuned horny sniper on a hunt. I admire her graceful poise and seductive bait, while packing an uncontrollable retard boner whipping around like a weed whacker.

I go stealth for positioning. The target is locked on.
The weapon goes hot.

- - -

The temperature is biting cold. The air stifling and thick. The roughshod streets exhale upward with rancid steam and rush hour stress. Brett enjoys the irony of the frenzied pace of freshly minted Russkies, whisking by in their sleek Italian Sports cars, Bentleys and Land Rovers. A shrewd cast of thug millionaires, they reek of Western gluttonous excesses, the very heritage and attitude  the oligarch entrepreneurs used to boldly claim to despise.

With their business ears to the ground, they've grown immune to the views of the statuesque bodies, their songs of virtuousness, crossing the Red Square with sophistication in luscious red thongs.

Emerging from the shadows, the coochie safari begins. Stealthy. Slippery. Brett executes the cocky casual strut with a loose precision, his blue balls clanking like brass Carillon Church bells. Cynical swagger. Clint Eastwood smirk. He angles straight towards this fine specimen. With each step, the view of the built for speed body vastly improves. The view of the girl improves too. Damn hot looking, even by Moscow's high standards.

She has warm melting green eyes above machete cheekbones. A classic thin nose, just aching for me to rest my sweaty balls on during hour five of GameCube. Her delicious bouncy rack is steered by swollen nipples, strapped down doubly tight in what must be some new titanium bra. Giant gazongas.

If she did a handstand, the planet would tilt off its axis.

With each sexy step of those CFM high heel stilettos, her hips whip side to side. Instinctively, Brett whips his head side to side in perfect synchronization, like a trained Peter North bobblehead doll.

Athletic. Tight. Butt. I want to pour salt on her ass and lick it. I want to talk to it, pet it, console it, and fall asleep on it snoring wet whistles with my nose.

- - -

She is a vision of purity; like virgin white flowers and songbirds announcing the spring season. Brett approaches her with all the grace of a turbo-charged, runaway Peterbilt dragging a muffler, while clenching in my fist a liver busting 16z Stolichnaya on the rocks from the bar I just left. A hand is placed gently around her waist. Brushing the unshaven face against the nape of her neck, I whisper dirty little nothings, and then nibble on her ear. She trembles, reverses direction and locks eyes. An afternoon of low expectations hints at decadence and deviance.

Will she choose pleasure or pain?

Her shadow on the sidewalk cannot hide the uncontrollable sexual beast inside her. She squints and hesitates, with a long, deafening pause…followed by a coquettish smile.

She loves every minute of it

Flashing a look up and down my foreigner physique, she does a quick inventory. As her cheeks turn scarlet red, the mood transforms into sparks of carnal anticipation, flying in both directions.

Whether she sees a compelling stud, or sexual mark to toy with, it's clear she approves. She leans forward. Whispering in my ear and giggling, her puffy nipples press tightly against the teal silk. I lean in to close in the deal, coolly using just 16 of my 80 memorized Russian words, ending the flirting with *Vi gavaritie pa Engliiski* (Do you speak English?) Hearing yes…it's checkmate.

Overseas, being aggressively playful always drops a woman's barriers, and the panties quickly follow. Either that or Boris the Brickhead boyfriend comes bounding round the corner to kick your ass, and you break into an Olympian sprint.

 Opening her eyes, she sees a raw, headstrong torpedo with just enough natural sheen to hide the snake oil. A look of both predator and prey. Brett's a charming rogue oozing confidence and success; a dashing caveman disguised as a gentleman in the occasional business suit. Securely attached to his Neanderthal attitude and appearance, he has shoulder length hair resting on bulging arms, the hands are often found in shady rock clubs wrapped around a sweaty Gibson Les Paul, ripping leads to no one and yet everyone…well, usually no one. Brett lives life at the pace of a Bonneville Salt Flats rocket. With testosterone backed up to the ears, shameless binge-drinking orgies can break out on any given night.

Women have been known to tell him "I've never felt so turned on and frightened at the same time."
He likes that. Brett scares little kids.
He likes that even more.

A vulture cackles in the distance. Out of the corner of my eye I see a newbie pickup artist in a loin cloth swinging from a vine, hoping to swoop in and steal the girl. Blinded by the steam from his gonads, he goes face first into a telephone pole.

I turn to the vulture. We coolly lock eyes and cynically nod. Later this week we'll smoke aged Cuban Cohibas, reminiscing about $3 Ho Chi Min blowjobs in dark alleys back in the 70's.

Ms. Hottie raises a finger and tickles the tip of my nose. I give her the Elvis sneer and my best bored as fuck impression. Pulse racing. Rod swelling, She runs her hand through my hair, leans in and plants a slow wet one on me.

Sensual. Borderline dirty.

She suggests a rendezvous drink, speaking softly in that sexy high girly girl Russian voice that makes your toes curl. Without a word, I open my hand. She places her tiny, soft palm in mine, squeezes it with a giggle, and reaches around and spanks my butt hard.

Spunky. I like that.

I'm not a perfume expert, but it smells like she's wearing that "fuck me till dawn" scent. Strolling hand in hand like lost lovers, a homing beacon pulls us towards the nearest happy hour in a trendy club a block away.

-   -   -

2.
NUKING THE EUROTRASH CAFE
...and the Roving Band of Poseurs

Entering the café we slip into a rear dark booth, as Brett prefers keeping the applause and autographs to a minimum. Always the sophisticated gentlemen, I order gigantic stiff drinks in Russian in a commanding Baritone voice, while snapping upskirts with my cell under the table. Double Kauffman Vodka Red Bulls, apple sour martini decanters, and an icy Unesco beer bucket appear on our table in a dry ice fog. Efficient speed seduction always begins with a rocket fuel party pack. The technique is designed to appear cosmopolitan, while getting hotties roadhouse tanked. Not a moment too soon, as conversation with females requires serious inebriation.

Just 6 more of these and you'll be gorgeous Brett!

This cafe is a bit away from my hotel, but it is always has great chick scenery, easy hookups, and a buffet of flaming idiots to insult.

Today is no exception.

Surrounded by liquor and a cynical disposition, we set up our observation shop and pass judgment on the sniffling group of poseurs like a Vogue Magazine Style Council.

A snobbish click of Euro-douches enter the scene, and acknowledge fellow greasy dweebs at a nearby table with revolting metrosexual screams. Both sexes greet each other with mmwah air kisses, preening and scanning the room desperately seeking attention. The girls speak with fake High Society accents in hushed tones, (*dawling for the chawnce to dawnce*), while the sassy sailors habitually consult their dinner plate-sized fake Rolexes. With tilted heads bobbing with the concerned raised eyebrow, the group pontificates in condescending elitist snippets, while expressing world-weariness and a pained sense of irony.

The predictable hot gossip includes imaginary ultra-fab trips to Monaco, Ibiza and the Mykonos Isles, snobbish reviews of the hottest "must-be-seen-in" restaurants and nightclubs, museum exhibits, art galleries, blah blah blah. As expected, a battle of fragile egos ensues, as they strain to one up each other. Threatening pinkies extend during boasts, while looking quite effeté sipping French piss-water Chardonnay. The scene looks straight out of an American Idol audition for the band DJ Douche-wipe and the STD's.

At the forefront of coolness, the douchebag leader leans in to speak. This self-anointed spokesman gives the airs of apparent affluence in cosmopolitan social circles, with two-tone aviator glasses, a slicked up pompadour 'do like a shark fin, and a silk gray designer jacket sans shirt exposing bling on the shaved chest. To be fair, Chadworth may have just left his shirt at an underground rave, having used it as a sperm wiper between BJs in a lineup. Each morning he spends seven hours in the mirror mastering the proper head tilt, while furrowing his girly eyelashes. Let's move on.

His bespectacled sidekick is a short bus greasy tool who resembles an over-animated puppet on crack, looking quite spiffy in the ironic T-shirt that should say *Smirking Smirkers who Smirk*. Jean Paul sports a sky high multi-colored roosterhawk that looks like Twizzler implants, waxed caterpillar eyebrows, and enough bling tats and 'tude it makes me want to grab him and charge the nearest door using his head like an ATF battering ram. This nutless eunuch attempts to dazzle the socialite girls with a lisping Renaissance faux-poet angle. After each preposterous boast, his face becomes tense, as he squeezes his butt cheeks to keep sperm from eeking out. Despite his best limp-wristed efforts, the girls ain't buying his shtick, so he's downgraded to market underperform.

Some sub-species knuckle-draggers hover at shoulder's length, peering on at the douche stars with googly puppy dog eyes of pure worship. Shuffling in sandals with white socks, they've got greasy Beatle's mop tops jelled with Chewbacca's sperm, massive overbites, Summer's Eve breath, and majestic lip herpes hood ornaments. In top

Euro conditioning, these ass-clowns have gone weeks without bathing, dressed like they've been dragged backwards through a sticker bush. A team belly flop into a pool and it's a Chocolate smoothie.

"Pigpen and Shaggy called, they want their dumpster skank back," I yell out with a bulging eyed Charles Manson grin, cracking my knuckles. They look up panicked. Blood. Pressure. Racing. Eyes bulge and stare down and away at the floor, a couple of stammering airheads fidgeting like little girls. A monkey could feed for a week picking creeping critters from their domes. Dying for acceptance from the Euro pack, they lean forward in a group stench cloud, idolizing the posse and their breathtaking phrases of imaginary nouveau rich coolness.

It's a Euro Poseur extravaganza! Our Vogue Style Council is roaring with laughter. Drinks are getting slammed like a 15 yr. old virgin at his first Rio Carnaval, while I stroke my date's cameltoe under the table. Time to shred the ladies....

T he chicks' wannabee leader holds court with a power-broking conversation about financial statements of imaginary suitors, suitcase-sized gold purses, and the sad plight of the Sardinian sea otter. Hiding behind enormous David Lee Roth sunglasses, Babs is a sniffling Israeli of ungenerous genes, with crinkly Brillo hair, a long canine face and dark peach fuzz mustache. Her sassy fashion statement is a screaming loud clashing gold/silver striped pantsuit doused with a gallon of eye-blinding perfume, a mirror medallion of discus proportions, all above cheap knock off designer shoes.

Bab's tacky act though, is all overshadowed by her giant hooked schnoz. She believes it accents her Middle Eastern heritage, but to any male christens her the love child of Bullwinkle and an Eastern Island statue. It's one big ass honker.

Large enough to cast shadows. Broad enough to give her a cross-eyed goldfish look. It forces hilarious tilted head angles as she laps at her almond-lemon-honey half-double decaf latte-espressacino. During sneezes she must use a parachute for that snot bazooka, otherwise you'd have customers pole vaulting and hanging on the chandelier, while the café floods in mere seconds.

When this loveable attention whore speaks, she's resembles an effervescent transsexual on crank. Any unfortunate visitors to her table are greeted with squeals and screams of elation bordering on awe. She screeches and clucks out their names before anyone else, determined to escalate her standing with the pack by soaking off the mere name recognition of others.

- - -

Looking to hook up, predatory dudes hover in the area and survey the female tenants on the menu, their attention focused entirely on the other girls at the table. Bab's dead gray eyes narrow with contempt while broodingly stirring her cappuccino, as she's routinely passed by. (*Don't you know who I am?!)* Nursing a vast and incomprehensible grudge, she's astonished at the phenomena of people not lusting for her and her high-rise bony jewish hips, Macau Parrot beak, and sticker bush hair scented with environmentally correct shampoo made of green apples, apricot and rain-forest soap.

Later tonight she'll cry a river while combing the perfumed hair on her precious Shih Tzu, promising little Fifi she'll call her parents Park Avenue analyst first thing tomorrow. The nerve!

- - -

Smug entitlement ass-i-tude written all over their faces, the other snippy socialites at the table do have a certain coked up vacuous sluts with high beams, BJ lips and perky ass appeal. Breeze flowing freely through their ears, between tiny pecks at finger sandwiches they manage to throw down "I Deep Throat" pouty glances. Twirling their hair. Bouncing the crossed leg. Adjusting the silicone. They're elitist cuties, but not exactly rocket scientists.

They're the girls you see standing in an Arbat Street Casino in front of a roulette wheel for an hour trying to buy a vowel. And as far as

Dawling joo know joo Vant me!

sex, they sadly lack the uninhibited Jenna genes. You know the type. Anorexic cultured Primadonnas who consider an hour of name dropping and worshiping the vanity foreplay. They scream out their own name during sex.

Following a dead high-maintenance lay, in the morning they wake up and deny anything happened, level your hotel room with a double-flush napalm dump, and then storm out; leaving you with a bewildered look beneath your oxygen mask, your skin infested with strange itching sensations, and your afternoon spent in a panicked emergency visit to the slimy Dr. Crotchrot.

-    -   -

By now Brett is roaring with laughter and chugging liquor double fisted, enjoying the table's disgusting elitist airs. Yet the possibilities are too rich. After my date hits the head, the first thought is to fill up a rusty bucket with a gallon of warm piss and dump it over their heads. Nah, too much work.

With my stomach painfully growling, the decision is easy. I'd just engorged some appetizers in a bar, which I was told were chicken nuggets, but with each bite I realized they looked and tasted more like fried golf balls dipped in lime green sewage. Overseas, tourists are an endless source of humor for restaurants. The special "Five Star Gringo menu" gets whipped out with a smile. Nods go around the waitstaff in a flash. Laughter is suppressed. You can hear a pin drop when I take the first bite.

They probably served me Raw Hairy Balls of Bison.

Within minutes, the meal ended with a deadly fumes in the face, horrid peanut-buttery roof of the mouth smacking, and the OMG ceremonial spitting out in a *Bleeeccchhhh* thud. Disgusting. For my troubles, they fed me a few Stolichnayas on the house. Not out of concern, but for the blowing chunks performance.

Time to nuke the Eurotrash. Pretending to slowly walk past, I back into the group inches away from their table and spray a gargantuan heated blast at face level in *Pffftt* silencer mode. It's a nuclear Russian Def Con 5 Fart; the kind so pungent and deadly even 400 pound men truly and profoundly fear enough to start jogging away from in a hurry. Even racing stripes would have been better than this Whopper. I loop around the room and wait at the bar a safe distance away. Down time six seconds. Sweat beads form on their girls' brows. Eyes light up with enraged fire. Nostrils flare. And then they swear at the sniffling, sneering Art Dicko poser and his posse and leave the table in a huff.

"A simple disapproval of the pâté would have sufficed. Really Chadworth! You're a beast….I never! Hummphfffff!".

-   -   -

S tanding at the bar, I impatiently tap fingers on the wood grain, waiting for a bartender to re-order two double vodka Redbulls. With my back turned, in an earsplitting shrieking tone of a seagull, I hear two women whining loudly about the numerous things they hate about men. Even from ten feet away, without looking I know they're enormous Amerikana touristas. Moscow is purgatory for western women. Even for the attractive ones, no man wants *anything* to do with them. Even homeless bums would turn down money for sex with them, considering the competition.

Next to me, a third US chunkette is singing *Don't you wish your girlfriend was hot like me.* I bust up laughing. She turns towards me, eyes light up, and babbles away in my ear about God knows what, stroking my forearm, trying to start up an *I'm sexy and sassy and loud and smell* conversation. Normally in these situations, I simply palm a hand grenade and threaten to pull the pin until they go away.

Do these girls own mirrors? Their cocky, noisy, beefy attempts at flirting have all the appeal of hooking up a lawn sprinkler to a septic tank. Anyway, she keeps pawing relentlessly at me and offers to buy me a drink, begging for attention. I suppose I could drop the pants and offer up some windy butt nuggets. Nah, not worthy. I'll settle for taking the high road. Being a distinguished gentleman, I'm quite versed in the finer cultural techniques of retiring from such a fine specimen of a woman as this. So I turn and say:

"I was in the supermarket the other day, and this chunky American girl was in front of me at the checkout. She had one Cosmo, one apple, one soda, one bag of popcorn, and one side of beef. So I leaned over and said:

"You're single aren't you?"

She said "Yes! How can you tell?!"

"Because you're ugly as fuck!"

As the look of horror crosses the fatties face, I remove her hand from my arm in silence, and walk ten feet to the other end of the bar, where I finally get a bartender's attention.

\-   -   -

A spunky teen tomboy in tattered Daisy Dukes with a hipster belt and S&M boots, observes the new tourist meat in the café. She makes a beeline towards my stuff. Tatiana is a ridiculously curvy thing of dreams, with smooth succulent thighs, long strawberry blonde hair cascading from beneath a teal bandana, and has a nympho sparkle in her eye that says *pick me, lick me, spank me, or I punish you*. Raw innocence and mayhem at once. I assume the cocky bored stance, secretly admiring her behind fogged over BluBlockers, with the wipers on slow delay.

She struts right up into my space to nibble on me and find out my story. By story, I mean she wants to use my face as an amusement park ride and have a side order of reverse cowgirl. She's a delicious slice of Nordic lust, probably grew up riding horses, climbing apple trees and beating up boys, until she found a copy of *Debbie does Vibrators* in her uncle's attic. By now she's gone through enough batteries that Energizer offered her a franchise.

"Mmmmm. Hi Sexy man! Are joo with girl, or ah joo available?" with a slow infectious smile curling her lips while she mauls my chest with her hands.

"That's still under negotiation" I coolly reply, picturing her bent over a tractor while I backdoor her in front of a herd of sheep screaming *Git her done Jethro!*

She presses her tight stuff against me, her eyes deep blue pools of young lust. Her lick-able smooth skin is the scent of strawberry fragrance combined with the soft musk of teen hormones. Young girls can never hide their horniness. She leans close to make sure I can feel the heat from her pussy through her clothes. I reach down and run my finger down the inside of the top of her shorts, and sure enough; no panties. (*bow chikka chikka bow bow*)

So I place a hand gently under her hair at the nape of her neck and pull her face to mine. She puckers with heavy lids. Fingertips stroke the top of her athletic thigh, gently grazing across her swollen mound and run up between her breasts, the index finger in her mouth. She sucks it on cue.

Bbbboooiinnngg.

A hyper-horny nymph, she makes an impressive pitch of her sexual urgencies that involve treating me like a piece of meat. I make an impressive attempt to stop staring at her high-rise camel toe and hear a word she says. It looks so juicy and nutritious. A wholesome well-balanced diet. Bon Appétit.

We trade sexual innuendos, recognize an immediate mutual interest in a sweaty threesome, but fate conspires against her good fortune. Before I can snag her digits and do the inappropriate butt grope, my first babe returns hissing her away.

Tomboy Hottie #2 removes her hips pressed against mine. As she backs away, I salute her with tent pants. Erections have no shame. They can be so inconvenient, particularly at senior bingo halls, funerals, and kindergarten playgrounds. Hottie #1 brushes aside the competition, and drags me BY MY WOOD back to our table, the triumphant lioness reclaiming her afternoon meal. All we needed was some Boogie Nights wah-wah on the jukebox and a porno could have broken out right then and there.

We sit.

Now that I'm eight drinks deep and have been tragically coerced into conversation, I switch to auto-pilot. The listening brain set to flat line mute, I allow her to tell me *her* story, which oddly enough lacks Tatiana the horny Tomboy. We sit across from each other at a wobbly table under neon mood lighting, (cue Celine Dion ballad), two heart torn soul mates reunited, destined for candlelight dinners, tantalizing sunsets, tears of pain and joy, followed by sloppy hair-yanking public blowjobs. Her eyes lock onto mine, full of adventure, heartache, and sexual undercurrents. It's quickly determined she's a talker looking for a reassuring listener, so I simply nod, refresh her drink, nod…refresh her drink. Nod…

She talks about the historic influence of Moscow architecture and museums and ballet and theatre and singing in the Sunday choir in St. Basil's Cathedral. I tell her she's a special woman, while picturing myself slapping my rod on her face for not putting ESPN on quick enough. Bad Nympho! Bad!

She tells me of her dark side; her favorite clubs, music, male body parts, and her overwhelming, uncontrollable obsession with sex on X. I pretend to pick lint off her blouse and tweak her nipple, while swizzling her drink with a glass dildo.

She tells me about her boring job, her boss the jerk, her mutant family, and the infinite struggles to survive in this harsh cruel world. I nod frequently and pretend I care, while checking out the boobalicious hoohas on the chick behind her. Glancing at her delicate fingers I smile; chicks with thumb rings do anal first date. It's a rule.

After what seems like days, the five minute conversation ends. She leans over and whispers; "Joo make da poosy hot" and swallows an ecstasy pill. I fall in love. Check please.

We hail a cab and go screaming off towards my love hotel, while behind the back I press the red button on my Blackberry and call in a eurodouche air strike.

The only thing we have in common is Oxygen and Lust.

3.
MOSCOW
A DANGEROUS INTOXICATING BEAST

Moscow is pulsating with unpredictable energy.

A chaotic surreal combination of Sex in the City meets the Beverly Hills Mafia. A cold hearted place of beauty, crime, and volcanic attitude, where you've never felt so alive, and so completely terrified at the same time. The country has condensed a century of cultural change in the last decade, with unprecedented success for the elite chosen connected few with the right bloodlines, dirty connections, or marksmanship.

Moscow is ranked the *most expensive city in the world,* home to the most billionaires, and over 100,000 millionaires. Billions of petrol-dollars have liquefied into capitalist excesses, and solidified yet another generational iron-fist legacy of ancestral control. The city's movers and shakers ooze sleaze and deceit through the pores of everything they touch. With such a backdrop of imminent peril and obscene costs, the sane observer would pose the logical question.

Why the hell go there?

Moscow's bandit capitalism overflows at the seams with crazed, adrenaline-driven excesses, dishing out a surreal blow to the senses. With his lecherous compadres joining in the debauchery, Brett exploits the town like a Porn comic book hero; a nymphomaniac caveman disguised in a business suit.

This cosmopolitan city is the prime hunting grounds for seducing some of the most absolutely fucking slamming, face melting gorgeous women on the planet. A city with more hotties per square inch than anywhere in the world. Dazzling women with a primal lust for instant gratification; models who will sleep with you after a 15 minute conversation to help pay for a Prada purse, plastic surgery or simply because they're bored. An image driven city that has adopted the fashion labels, hip music, and sexual exploitation from the West, but they execute them with an intense fanaticism, uniquely their own.

Moscow is the ultimate pussy pilgrimage.

The Ironman triathlon of sex, danger, and adventure. Russian girls are like no other women you will ever meet; smoldering eye contact everywhere you look, strutting and propositioning you in malls and all over town, butt grabbing and wandering hands in your lap in bars.

But to solely lust their gorgeous faces and tight body parts is selective observation, just admiring the bricks while ignoring the mortar holding it altogether. They're witty, intelligent, crazed spontaneous, and yet still deliciously feminine.

Not a PC bone in their bodies.
No sexually repressed desires.

Wild lost souls.
Sex is like breathing to them.

Inside the Kremlin Walls

But it's more than that though. It's their attitude; their devious hair on fire insanity. Hyperactive. Sexually curious, and acting on every impulse. That's the icing on the cake.

They live for *what the fuck* adventures full of risk and vice. They practically never say no to anything.

Moscow.
Where the price is high and the prize is priceless.

For first trip newbies, we're talking giggling, OMG uncontrollable High School hard-ons every five minutes. And that's just in church. For flat out adventure, there is nothing like popping in here to absorb the iron fist culture, cruise through 500 year old cathedrals bombed on top shelf vodka, boning a dozen supermodels, and fleeing town in the dead of night like a sexual escape artist.

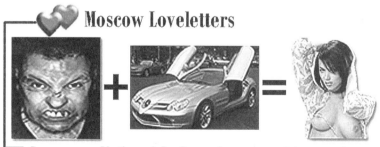

Moscow Loveletters

Gorgeous, distinguished gentleman seeking soulmate. Must love Theatre, the Arts, and be a Fuck Machine.
Bring Vodka and girlfriends

4.
DEEP ORAL HIGHWAY DURING A POLICE CHASE

... We return to our regularly scheduled story already in progress

Our crusty old Volga Taxicab races down Tverskaya, dragging a rusted muffler that sounds like a Civil War cannon. It's a decrepit 60's beast quite at home in the bowels of Moscow, showing 200,000+ km on a Speedo long since broken and caked in slime. The busted heater blasts cold dusty morsels of choking dead air. As for the shocks, they're years past their last legs, like the scaly legs on the old MILF hookers with deep empty eyes and twats like a 20 yr. old catcher's mitt, hovering on street corners praying for blurry eyed customers.

The driver, who's drunk and smells like a boxer's greasy armpit, shows little skill navigating the old decaying side streets. Bottoming out in the deep potholes, we hear screeching metal scraping pavement, followed by pole vault leaps out of the ruts, sending us airborne and doing head butts off the drooping headliner.

The bucket of bolts Taxi becomes irrelevant noise though, as things accelerate quickly with Natasha the Supersnatch. As she crawls all over me with CFM eyes, I nibble on her smooth warm neck, her scent sweet and musky, and feel her blood pulsating through her veins.

Her fingertips pinch my nipple, and venture down and start stroking the Johnson. She looks at me deep with her bedroom eyes and tongues her lips, purring dirty little nothings. The windows in the cab steam up like we're driving in a Cape Cog fog.

A squeaky girly girl giggle later, she lifts her short skirt and yanks her teenie lace thong down those long slender legs. I sneak a peek at her smooth bald mound and wet pink smile. As she gazes at me through heavy lids, she strokes her erect clitoris and slips a finger inside, moisture seeping from her swelling vulva. She moans softly with a series of small tremors, and slides over straddling my leg, riding and rubbing her warm honey hole against my thigh.

She kisses me. First with sexy little soft dry touches. This rapidly accelerates into a full 440 volt perverse tongue assault. Sliding down and off my leg, her moist *pizda* leaves a slick snail trail on the top of my thigh. Without a care in the world, she unzips my fly and slides down the pants to mid-thigh. Reaching her hand under the waistband

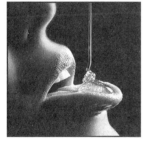

of my shorts, she lowers her head.

Brett coolly pauses until she's officially halfway down the rod, and then instinctively clicks his stopwatch for the official time. Exactly 5 hours and 19 minutes in town before the first blowjob. A half hour longer than last trip, but I'll take it.

My Russian friends will later laugh at the slow results, disapprovingly shake their heads saying…

"Not good Brett…less Passion, more Aggression!"

-   -   -

While the babe's locks bob up and down, Brett glances up and spies the frail skanky cabbie adjusting his rear view mirror to get a better view of the action. With the fixed gaze of a dingo, he gives a gross and way-too-creepy rotted teeth smile and winks. I shift my eyes out the window repulsed and hope the assclown goes away. Eventually returning my eyes, I see he's angled the rearview mirror down at the chick's lips and my stuff, as she does her magic. He turns and nods his head at me, cackling with a sweaty brow while licking his lips.

"It turns its skeezy face around and watches the road."

What are the friggin' odds of this happening? I'm in the most macho country in the world, full of thugs and gangsters, and end up with a flaming cabbie who's gone prematurely gay. I feel a sense of potential nausea, and if Mr. Vomit visits the scene, I know exactly where to aim. Silly boy. Dicks are for chicks. Any minute now he's going to break out into a chorus of *Glory Glory Hole-alujah*.

"Say Bruuuce, what'ya say we dump the bitch off and go cruising for transvestites?" I ask in my best ball-peen-hammer-to-your-face expression.

"*You . ah . one . ugly . muthafucka*" yells the ticked off Johnson before disappearing back into the hotties mouth.

Skankman gives one more fruitcake glance in the mirror and I've had enough. I reach down and zip up the fly. Suddenly the cab lurches hard left, hurtling down a decrepit cobblestone side street. Sensing an immediate problem, I grab his shoulder and yell "*you're going the wrong way!*""

He spits out insults under his breath, taunting me with a slimy gaze in the rear-view mirror. Then he punches it, accelerating down steep winding turns in a death defying slalom that sends us bouncing like pinballs off the brittle rusted door panels. My date screams "*Svoloch blyad!*" (fucking bastard) and unknown swears in lightning fast Russian, which brings a black snaggletooth grin and laughter from the bug eyed cabbie.

Then the unmistakable foreign police car sirens begin…. *dee-dooo-dee-doooo*. The cabbie floors it and we go whipping around a corner and screaming down a final straightaway, with the cops in hot pursuit on our tail. It's like that scene out of the Pink Panther, through grungy streets barely one car wide.

The cab whipsaws through a hairpin turn, but on the next long straightaway the *militsia* rams our rear bumper. The cabbie surrenders, veering right and screeching to a sliding halt in a barren courtyard. My date starts bawling her eyes out, her face white like she's seen a ghost. Who knows what nightmares are in store for me?

We park in a deserted square, surrounded by abandoned crumbling granite block apartments and bombed out ruins from the Brezhnev era. Out the left window is a frozen fountain full of generic vodka bottles and inhumane industrial waste. Out the right window are tall birches and willows, long since iced over. As if on cue, the weather turns bitter cold, pelting down swirling, heavy golf ball sized snowflakes and hail.

Angry Russian snow.

Cars with headlights on in the afternoon roll on by uninterested, as an artic wind comes howling across the courtyard freezing my bones.

Joo Idiotz. Bring me dat Brett Tate before he steals *all* our women …

A door slams. The eerie silence is deafening.

-　-　-

Moments later, Brett is greeted by a Kalashnikov toting, pissed off uber polizia leering through the window. He rips open the door, and yanks me out by the shoulder, grinding his teeth and screaming in Russian. Chaw spits splatter on rocks kicked into the cab fender, the pungent shoe polish of their jackboots reeking heavily. The air fills with yelling and wild-eyed bizarre tirades from Vladimir and his smelly WWE looking partner, fingering his holster. Massive brutes oozing intimidation and pain out of every pore.

Pointing with their guns with an expression of absolute power, the cops separate the three of us to different spots. My hummer chick is parked inside the cop car. Not good. Judging by her violent shaking and gasping for air, she must fear rape by the whole force back at the station. My perfectly executed pull off the streets appears all but lost.

　The turn of events stinks like a whorehouse at low tide.

Standing in a frightened huddle, the skanky cabbie apologizes and rambles and pleads our case to the cops, which brings a chunky swat across the face. Every attempt of mine to get status brings a crescendo of screams and official demands, none of which I understand.

- - -

The massive Kremlin Wall

Russian cops specialize in humiliation, cruelty, and rage. The only thing they despise more than foreigners is a metrosexual coward, to whom they exploit with a special vindictiveness. The only defense is to be stone faced; show no fear and let it play out. Finally I get the *"your Papers"* request from the cops. They huddle reading them, sharing assorted throaty whispers and grunts. Handing them back, more screaming orders are barked in throaty Russian.

"Joo papers bad," the cabbie informs me, which I know is a total crock. I smell a scam… I hope. Normally they just bribe you and move on. This time it seems like I may be in serious trouble.

"Bullshit" I say, and both cops instantly point their machine guns inches from my face. Bad move. I stand stone faced. The gruff barrel-chested militza snags an iron grip of my collar, and drags me from the area to the near frozen river's edge, teetering on the lip. With raging waters and icy chunks whipping by at my feet, Boris the Brickhead holds me inches from falling, screaming at me while pressing his gun square into my lower back. A metallic click of his weapon signals readiness for combat. The asshole dishes out a little Vincent Price laugh, ramming the gun hard into the spine.

In the distance across the Krasnoholmsky Most Bridge, I see an abandoned Tsarist complex of massive vine covered buildings, dungeons and tombs; a post apocalyptic vision of eerie emptiness and a cold black chill. It mirrors my current situation. And so there I stand; staring into the lost pussy abyss. My options appear to be get shot and drown in the frozen river, or to jump in and drown in the frozen river. Quite a coin toss. A black vulture hovers overhead in descending circles, cackling in approval. The scene rivals a great Black Sabbath album cover.

The chance of endorsements for the triathlon pussy pilgrimage is looking mighty slim. Blasphemy! This must be how Caesar felt when the Roman Senate turned on him, seizing his throne, and selling Cleopatra to a Saudi Arabia brothel for two camels, and a playmate to be named later.

Brett always figured he'd go out with style and grace. Living on an undiscovered Asian Island, it would be a noble death. The insatiable Adonis falls during an orgy, laced with Viagra, Colombian flake and top shelf booze, surrounded by a human pyramid of naked young bodies chained to a bed.

Instead some flathead barbarian wants to shoot me and watch me float off into the sunset, a gurgling, stiffening human bobber. In moments of pure desperation, the body's natural defense mechanism takes over. The King Cobra will rise 8 feet and spit deadly venom in your eyes.

"Komrade; these strict new standards for Kremlin Guards are cruel & unusual punishment."

When cornered, the stingray shoots saw-edge poisonous barbs. As for me, I have no choice but to resort to one final desperate measure with my most powerful weapon available. Not to say it was planned. Out of sheer panic, from deep down in my bowels I accidentally unleash one more death defying Balls of Hairy Bison fire-breathing-fart, which catches a gust of wind and blows straight up the cop's nostrils and into his mouth. The cop starts gagging and lowers his weapon. Seizing my advantage, I spin around and decide to roll the dice while his guard is down.

"*Mozhet dogovorimsya*?" while shuffling some bills in the wallet. (sort of like saying "let's talk about this.")
"A policeman life eez difficult, salary berry small" he says. And then with a bitter beer face and a sense of urgency to step away from the swamp cloud, he counters with "$200 US."

I carry money in multiple places on the body, and visibly open the wallet and hand over the entire $50 I keep in it, valuing my life at $150. In seconds I hear "DONE!" So it was just about money, he just felt like taking the fear a step further. What a prick.

The barrel-chested cop pulls me away from the icy waters edge, and speed walks back to his cruiser, coolly transforming into his natural bribe-happy state.

In a ginormous final clash, the Viagra Stud takes down Flathead Pigasaurus in a Moscow smackdown spectacular. I hand him the money and we stroll on back to the car. He opens the polizia door and hands me back his ace-negotiating card, *der blonde with da hot poosie*. Slamming the doors and gunning the engine, they spit out "stupid Americana", cackling as they split the money, and continue a conversation *in English!*

While laughing their asses off, they treat us to a Starsky and Hutch 360° burnout out of the area, spraying dirt, and broken bottles in our face. Bagman and Rob'em split the scene.

As they pull away, I scream out *"we kicked your hockey team's ass in the 80 Olympics",* but they were long gone. As I turn towards the cabbie, I notice he too is smiling with glazed over eyes. Remembering his unexplained turn down side streets makes it all clear to me. The asshole was in on the whole thing.
Lesson learned.

This whole event is just one big game to them. Breaking out an old habit, I memorize his license plate: A009DS, as in **A** (009) **D**ick Smoker. Easy enough.

Speeding out of the area we navigate the streets and cruise up to my hotel. Blondie dishes out electric kisses and molests my re-invigorated wood the whole ride, while politely ignoring the final bursts of swamp clouds seeping out my pants.

The Vegas odds are soaring on the nooner being salvaged after all! Good thing. I'd hate settling for a token courtesy hummer. Exiting the cab, the hotel security guards take one look at Brett the Gringo's afternoon hottie kissing and fondling me, and they promptly go straight into the same bullshit; denying her an entrance. Soon I hear *"dere's a problem with her papers."* In silence, I snatch her papers from their hands, replacing them with a cupped $20 bill handshake.

Damn. This is hard work.
The whole friggin' city is on the take.

En route to the infamous Christ the Savior Cathedral
alongside the Moskva River and Kremlin Walls

5.
BOOTIE AND THE BEAST
DO THE WALK OF SHAME

Strutting through the lobby, all heads turn to see der horny supermodel strut her stuff. It's the cheapskate happy hour, so we stumble into a full house of past-their-prime salesmen slobbering like famished coyotes behind fogged up shades the size of garbage can lids. With one just shake of her perky ass, mixed drinks are tilted back and stop short of the chins, spilling down their striped mid-chest ties, and splashing into the pocket protectors. The front desk babes are all waves and smiles, checking out the chick competition. Sizing up my *date*, winks go around, and my room number is marked for potential late night, full-contact room service.

Passing the hotel lounge bar, the hottie kisses me and cups my butt, loving the attention. As for the respectable tourist couples observing the free show, the chunky opinionated wives smirk in vile disgust at Bootie and The Beast. Several wobble around, and launch into wild-eyed rag sessions to their nodding, tuned out husbands, infuriated about being forced to watch this embarrassing Walk of Shame.

Silly Cattle. For Brett, this is the Walk of Fame.

The husbands stand tall for the first time in a decade, adjusting their toupees while flashing horrid green toothy grins that look more like

Steven Hawkins muscle spasms. In their hands, frightened beer bottles are choked in the steel grip of a sexually repressed Preacher. While their wives seethe in jealous rages, the men strain to keep a non-committal face and not get busted gawking, while dreaming of humping Natasha's leg and shooting their wife *and* her fucking little French poodle with the pink bows and gay perfume.

As for the old widowers, the days of hiding things and giving two shits have long since passed. Back in the day was three bourbons ago. Brows furrowed, they adjust their dog-eared fur hats and rapidly blink to make sure she's not a mirage. Then they smack their gums, paint chin dribble and groan heartily, staining their Depends.

As we stroll towards the elevator area, a repulsive collection of western fatties have vigorously plunged headfirst into a buffet feed trough. Rhinos, Hippos, Water Buffalo, Elephants. What? Is this Animal Planet? Is Noah's Ark valeted out front? What cruel Underworld deity chose to forklift them into my world?

We carefully navigate around the perimeter of the lobby to avoid getting eaten, as the unholy scene unfolds.

In your dreams you skinny fuck!

In the buffet line, a wall of opinionated sloppy monsters leer with scowling pit bull faces, going for that sexy Murderers row chorus line look that makes my knees go weak. A few fatties elbow each other and point, their massive droopy triceps swinging and slapping loudly against their enormous torsos, spraying sweat onto heaping plates of lard. Each platter is held with raised pinkies, with a daintiness preposterous to their girth. After hurling insults, they attack the sides of beef on their plates with the fierceness of hand-to-hand combat.

Several vultures circling above the greedy herd vomit at the foul sight, and flip them off as they flee the scene.

When one poor husband makes the fatal mistake of reaching for a single celery stick, two Brontosauruses whip around and crush him with their keg bellies, holding him airborne by his bald head alone, his feet spinning madly in the air riding an invisible unicycle.

Gorgeous BBWs they are, in their Coleman tent dresses, triple chin beards, orange peel Titleist thighs and cankles. The back of their necks look like a pack of hotdogs. Have I slipped into a six dimensional phatosphere and been damned into eternal fatnation? The sight is surely enough to make a warthog dry heave. Maybe it's a commercial for Pepto Bismol…for warthogs.

-    -   -

One particularly gargantuan beast is decked out in a gigantic lime green pantsuit that could double as a car cover, going for that sexy 500lb Teletubby-hot-air-balloon look that unleashes global hard-ons. The rear flap attempts to cover a double-wide rump so enormous it deserves its own zip code; it's hard to tell where the ass ends and the cankles begin. She has tufts of porcupine whiskers tangled with leftovers on her chin, and a gigantic bucket head dotted with sparse patches of hair that looked like something a cat coughed up.

Ms. Tonnage is hissing and leering at us, full of cocky fat-itude. She makes a point of barking a bit too loud to her beaten down suicidal husband, in that shrieking enraged voice so typical of chunky western women;

"Why she's young enough to be his daughter!" while peering down into a freshly emptied KFC bucket in her paws. Eyes bulging in sheer panic, she starts gnawing on the cardboard in a virtual feeding frenzy.

Screeching to a halt, she receives Brett's heartwarming reply.

"I take offense to that Shamu. She's far closer to being my granddaughter. And let me add, having witnessed first-hand the size of your ass, I believe I speak for the *entire* male species when I say Holy Fuck!"

Then I wink at her slouching, tail dragging husband and reach down and stroke Natasha's cameltoe. And then sniff my finger.

We strut to the elevator.

In horror, the rotund monster drags her mumbling old man away, while he wets his finger and mats down his comb-over back into place. Nice helmet buddy. Later in bed he'll cringe listening to her re-live the episode over and over. As her role takes on ever increasing delusions of prominence, he quietly downs a liter of warm Jack Daniels. One hand holds the bottle; the other hand fingers the cold steel of a butcher knife under the pillow.

Blabbing and clucking away to the wall, his cute bride will chomp down an incidental 12000 calories, occasionally rolling and pinning him under her ass, muffling his panicked death gurgles and screams. For dessert, she'll toss him like a rag doll on top of her gut, and force another sad round of drunken impotent sex with her belly button. If she wants it while on her belly, he'll rent a mule for that long, slow, bumpy ride down to the bottom of her ass crack.

Then again, it's hard for him to argue, since she does serve an important purpose in his life, acting as a much-needed anchor for their untethered mobile home in the eye of tornadoes. But if you listened closely, he's whispering *"must buy .50 caliber hunting rifle, get speedy divorce and return. Yes! I will return."*

Nearing the elevator, I glance back at the cellulite spectacle. It looks like an outtake from Clive Barker's *Nightmare on Whale Street.* Spotting the enormous green balloon supported by keg legs, I contemplate dropping a 50 lb bag of cement from the atrium's 30th story onto that monstrous thick skull of hers, the bag exploding in a white cloud as she waddles away, clueless of my gallant attempts of elephanticide.

\-   \-   \-

One of my favorite traits in Russian women; no matter how classy and sophisticated they appear, deep down they're all uninhibited sexual freaks. Born exhibitionists. Contrasted with tattooed white trash spring break hogs flashing sloppy tits and keg bellies with their deafening *"woo hoo"* mating call, you can't wait to see these lean Russian bodies exposed.

As we enter the glass-encased elevator, she slides her panties off, and presses her pouty lips passionately against mine in a full assault, tongue-sucking, red-lipped fellatio. As the elevator starts to rise, she giggles and lifts her dress to her neck. Pressing her gorgeous naked body against the glass facing the hotel lobby, she flashes the shrieking cattle below.

Several husbands look up with trembling lips, alligator tears streaming down their cheeks, and splashing the tent poles in their pants. All 30 floors up she holds the flash position, while doing a behind the back reach around stroking my rod;

"Brett, joo make da poosy steaming hot. I'm going to fuck joo like cowboy."

A nice touch.
Giddy-up.

Watcha da truck Boris, I'll be right back.
Da new Hustler just arrived.

6.
FOR YOUR THIGHS ONLY

Racing into the hotel room, Natasha kicks her high heels off, slides down her coral blue miniskirt and red thong, and high tails it into the bathroom like there's a fire. Her awkward stride gets zero style points, but I'll give her a 7.5 for the bouncing shaved snapper view. As her out-of-tune Cristina Aguilera singing echoes off the shower walls, I race to the room fridge and crack some beers, a seasoned traveler protecting the first day's binge drinking status. Viagra popped; the nuts growl and fill with ammo. The weapon goes hot.

A fog of steam, perfume and body lotion scents float through the air, as my nooner is finally coming to fruition. Wrapped loosely in a towel, she slithers out of the bathroom on her tan tippytoes. All thoughts focus on the Natasha Show. Representing the Ukrainian Porn Industry, she climbs under the sheets, all puckering lips and slippery hips. As I snatch the towel away and start giving her a back massage, it becomes immediately obvious this hot little number has one *astonishing* sex drive.

As my hands slide lower and barely touch the top of her butt, she starts moaning and scrambling and crawling around like a caged lion. This repeats with increasingly more volatile reactions, with every stroke closer to her honey hole. I spin her over, and find her rack is like turning on a TV. Tweaking the left nipple turns her power on, and the right nipple adjusts the volume. She simply has fire in her blood, like a wild animal in heat.

Moving in, I spread her meat flaps, like a horny gynecologist fulfilling sticky finger cheerleader fantasies. Out of respect, before the meal begins,

I bow and say grace; (an old habit from crazy Aunt Mildred with the high rise blue hair, Coke bottle glasses, and skin that needs ironing). As my tongue starts exploring within inches of Natasha's magic button, her hips thrust madly; she unleashes animalistic guttural wailing deafeningly loud. For a moment I back off, as the volume is becoming a bit alarming.

As in FUCKING LOUD!

There's no stopping this beast. She grabs my hair and yanks my head down in search of a finale. Her young pussy is all that and then some, with subtle scents of an Ibiza ocean breeze and the sweet taste of a late summer mango. As her moaning becomes even more frenzied, her head thrashes maniacally. When she nails Big O #1, she comes like a steam locomotive, thrusting her hips upward so hard, I thought her pussy broke my nose! Imagine explaining that to the old lady when you get back from your business trip.

"Well dear, I was shopping for duty free spices, and the strangest thing happened…"

Her body jerks spastically as she shudders into multiple Big O #2

and #3. The screaming is shattering windows, closet doors are ripped off their hinges, walls are cracking, the bed rises a foot from the floor, and the guests in the next room are probably reporting a rape or murder taking place. She curls up into a little orgasm ball, convulsing. Any follow-up touching of the coochie brings earth shattering orgasms, screaming and shaking and yelling and squirting. I fully expect the building to go airborne, and see Dorothy peddling by the window in sperm covered lingerie, on her way to Emerald City to get a rabbit vibrator from the Wizard of Oz.

 As Natasha finally settles down for a moment, she shoves me aside, rips my pants off and takes control. Slow, sensual foreplay is not in her playbook. Not a chance. She lowers her head and goes straight into hardcore turbo-sucking, like a flesh-starved zombie. Eyes locked on mine as she licks and bobs. Occasionally, she withdraws my rod with a wet popping sound, and slaps it against her face whispering slutty promises of things she's going to do to me, and then dives back down the shaft deep. The girl is simply on fire. I get the full dirty oral package of sloppy, slurping, sucking, pumping, and hand twisting with deep throat suction, a performance that has my toes curling and ass rising in the air.

- - -

It's a long way from my US women a decade past, where BJ foreplay is yapping and nagging and dishing out guilt trips like it's a lost art. In a nutshell, they won't do much of anything, and they do it poorly. Blowjobs? They're like a bad SNL skit.

Starting and stopping every 15 seconds. No rhythm to it.

They lap at it like they're painting a picket fence.

All the romance of a quadriplegic tooting on a harmonica.

I generally wait a few minutes into the hummer and just tell them to stop; otherwise I'll start snoring, or feel the urge to pee. The only relief I feel is when I see their ass leaving out the door. Then I dress up my vacuum cleaner in lingerie, and sort out which lips attachments to use. Am I feeling tight-lipped Scandinavian, or another plate-lip turbo-sucking trip to Zimbabwe?

B y contrast, within 30 seconds with Natasha I'm saying *"wo wo wo...slow down honey"* for fear of losing it too soon. This hot little *dyev* sucks it so hard the bed sheets go up my ass.

I push her head away, shove her over and smack her ass, letting her know it's time for the Doctor to take over. She smiles devilishly and says *"I been berry bad girl, hurt me Daddy."* I look on with paternal love, as she follows it up with a gymnastic flip and pins her ankles behind her ears and hits me with *"fuck me hard"* commands. I bend down for a quick lick taste test of the honey levels, and find the pussy machine is ripe and ready.

Starting on top, I plan an initial slow building crescendo of missionary pumping to try and keep the noise to a minimum. After a couple halfway in pumps while licking her neck, she screams in Russian and punches me with an Evander combo hard in the chest. BBbaamm! THWOK! KAPPOWW! Then she grabs my ass and thrusts upward demanding speed.

"I vont fuck NOW!" Quite the romantic girl, this one.

Natasha has no interest in an underwhelming, clockwatching western sex approach from a sense of duty. She intends to take as much as she can from me. Push me over the edge. Twisting and humping and kicking all night in sweat-drenched bed sheets. Riding this girl is like breaking in a colt. There really is nothing I can do to stop her. The Horrors!

She flips me over and goes straight into a rapid fire cowgirl, riding and engulfing me breaking speed records. After an earsplitting orgasm or five, she spins into reverse cowgirl, and starts pumping while reaching back around and fingering her ass, whimpering and howling at the top of her lungs. I'm both turned on and scared shitless, as I'm hitting bottom and know all too well you can break your dick in this position. But the girl is a damn professional. I'm just along for the ride.

I flip her over into doggie style position, hand her a pillow to bite and muffle the moans, while admiring this exquisite piece of ass.

Ouch, what a view. Tight lickable stuff. The sexy contoured back. The treasure trail of blonde hairs above the bootie crack. Her silky smooth skin is tantalizing, but the whole porno instincts and uncontrollable attitude, the animal hunger really starts turning me on.

Not one to disappoint, I put on the devil horns, ram into her hard, and pop the clutch from 1st to 4th gear. As the turbo kicks in, I say fuck it and push the nitrous button, and transform into Brett the Beast…an orgy crazed monster banned in

several countries. Let the pounding begin. All details of what happen from here on will be denied, and questions will be forwarded to my attorney.

The next hour was more of a bizarre fetish-fest than erotic. One of the more violent sessions in recent memory, during which I lost what little dignity I had left, not to mention five pounds of sweat. We covered all the textbook positions, all the freak positions, and made up a few of our own. Highlights? Early on during the violent doggie style, she turned around and asked "are joo into dildos?"

"Not really, it's kind of hard to walk the next day."

She laughs, and out of her purse in David Copperfield fashion she pulls out a vibrating dildo that looks like a softball bat. The thing has about ten gears, and is so big I have to kick start it.

"I like deez in da ass."

I take the sex harpoon, and not to be outdone, wave a magic wand and pull a quart of 10W40 and a funnel out of my ear, and fill up her exit hole. Lying in the 69 position on my back, I bury my face in her succulent dripping lips, and starting ramming the dildo as hard as I can into her ass. It's the brilliant Porn Star move #436, rarely attempted in the eastern bloc. After about ten seconds, she squeals and slams her cookie down into my face so hard, I nearly suffocate.

This move was not covered in the porn instruction manual, and represents a serious pussy foul. But I'm a patient man.

All efforts hints to elevate her and breathe are silenced and muffled, as she pushes down hard and screams and comes over and over. Finally I have to bench press her whole body in the air to survive. Tossing her like a blow up doll onto her stomach, I pop up panting for air. Resuming in the doggie style position, I switch the weaponry and shove the dildo in her pussy and slam my ribbed condom sausage in her ass. Why a ribbed condom? It gives you better traction in the mud.

This isn't one of those bleary eyed drunken bum-rapes, with coaxed entries full of sugar coated lies about it not hurting. "Come on honey; no brain…no pain".

This is dry animal butt sex. Manly. Raw. I feel like I'm starring in Pulp Friction. I can't say it surprised me when she says she likes it rough. Of all the women I've had the pleasure of being molested by, Russian women are the kinkiest. They like it violent, hard, and fast. They like to get spanked, slapped, tied, hit, bit, kegs rolled over their shins, you name it, and they'll do it.

She asks for me to blindfold her. Then she asks for her wrists to be loosely tied behind her back. Laced with Viagra and vodka, I could poke a hole through concrete. She receives a relentless sweat drenched, knee scuffed, 3-hole jackhammer treatment that should have put her in a wheelchair, to the point that it frankly embarrassed me, (not that I stopped). We're talking ruthless full speed back-door pummeling, while yanking on her Kournikova ponytail reins, and slapping her ass beat red. I even took my eye off ESPN highlights during half of it. The girl has incredible stamina and is completely insatiable. It was like we crossed some invisible sex barrier I didn't even know existed. At one point she even begged for Schindler's Fist. I passed. I like to keep a clean hand free, in case I feel like picking my nose or giving her a dirty Sanchez.

For the finale of this violent slam-a-thon, I flip her over, pull out and paint a thick white landing strip from her bellybutton all the way up to the base of her chin. Peter North would have applauded everything but the short landing.

What can I say? I'm a cultured gentleman. I rarely give a facial after the first fuck. My nuts are practically sucked inside my body. I catch a glimpse in the bedside wall mirror; I have the jetfighter G force cheeks going, veins popping, and between the pussy juices and sweat, it looks like I'd dumped my face in a popcorn bowl full of Vanilla ice cream and Vaseline. Gross! ...but my hair was perfect.

Blondie falls asleep for an hour, while I raid the room bar, order up some room service and catch the tail end of MLB web gems. She's a restless sleeper, spinning around constantly, while pressing her warm body against mine. Finally she curls up dead to the world. The sexual tension that marked her face vanishes. She looks perfectly tranquil, finding peace after a long strenuous round of sweaty sex with a big scary man.

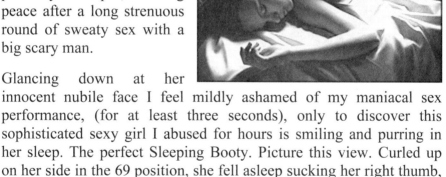

Glancing down at her innocent nubile face I feel mildly ashamed of my maniacal sex performance, (for at least three seconds), only to discover this sophisticated sexy girl I abused for hours is smiling and purring in her sleep. The perfect Sleeping Booty. Picture this view. Curled up on her side in the 69 position, she fell asleep sucking her right thumb, while her left hand holds my warm rod pressed against her cheek.

Like a hard earned trophy.

Eventually she flips over and buries her head between my shoulder blades making soft whimpering noises. She bats her long eyelashes at me and wraps her warm curvy stuff into my arms, being more cuddly and sweet than any sane girl should ever be with a man like me.

Gazing at me with innocent doe eyes that I never saw before, she whispers in my ear; "I hope joo find it."

"Find what?"

"Joo know…vott-ever it eez joo looking for. Joo have dat look."
She rolls over and goes back to sleep.

- - -

Finally the room service knock comes. I wrap myself in a towel and sprint to the door to see which hottie is delivering the grub. It turns out it's the sexy one with perky, lickable tits…they all look like that. Ahh, it's the sensual Veronika, a previous conquest on a prior visit to the hotel. She invites herself in with the tray, and puts it on the bedside table. Seeing the babe sleeping in bed, she walks straight over and slowly peels the sheets back, checking out her deliciously smooth shaved kitty.

"Mmmmmm. Nice poosie."

Instant hard-on.

Brett signs the bill, leaving her an enormous rubles tip. She kisses me on the lips, and turns to leave with a big smile. I expected more than that. She walks three steps, spins around and yanks my towel off, staring me down with her horny bedroom eyes and a thirsty tongue traveling around her wet lips.

Taking her top off, she bends down cupping Mr. Happy for a sexy blowjob sampling for five minutes. I take it out of her mouth and give a playful slap in the face with it.

"Less Passion, more Aggression!"

"I sorry, da beeg boss eez downstairs. I work-a-da late shift tonight, Mr. Brett. Joo call me for room service call and I can finish deez meal."

"Don't hold your breath, honey" says the Johnson.

I tweak her nipple and walk her to the door naked. She holds my dick for the stroll, her eyes never leaving it. Opening the door, she pauses, and slowly walks away without breaking her dick eye contact. I lean out and watch her work that ass down the hallway. Damn Russian women can strut their stuff.

Hottie on the bed pops up and joins me for the meal. During it, she tells me about her sad, desperate life in Siberia that she left behind growing up without parents, spending -40°F winter days sleeping on the floor hugging the radiator for warmth. Shit, I didn't know she planned on speaking.

I obsessively inspect battery on the iPOD, nodding frequently.

"We have nothing. No work. No food. Nothing."

I consider window parachute jumping to flee the conversation. Maybe the S&M slapping, bowlegged anal was a good time for her.

Peeking through the curtains, the shrinking sun's shadow across the sleeping glass skyscrapers announces nightfall all too soon, and this Coochie Bandit has an evening of wretched debauchery to take care of. Sadly, it's time to kick Natasha's ass out without a second round. I sit on the edge of the bed and watch her slowly dress, drooling like a caveman with a T-Rex bone in my mouth. Yummy. She pours that killer body back into the coral blue miniskirt. She bends over and let's a boobie fall out while she slips on the high heels, making sure I get a good whiff. It works. I get a déjà vu hard-on. Damn. What a piece.

As we leave the hotel room, she pushes me against the door and smothers me one last kiss. Slow. Sensual. Like old lovers. Ouch. I'm going to remember this one. She's something special. A girl could really do some damage to my heart, if I wasn't such a drunk narcissist sex addict with a five second memory span. She writes her cell number down while I slip a healthy parting gift into her purse.

Walking her out the front door of the hotel, I get warm all over just watching her snap that rock hard ass as she strolls away. My head bobs again side to side in perfect synchro, while I breathe in a final whiff of her perfume. Damn, what a piece.
Off into a bubblebutt sunset.

Keep me smiling for a decade.

The chick and I made plans to hook up again later on in the week, but due to scheduling conflicts (dick in other hotties), it never happens.

-   -   -

Laughing to himself, a dapper old coot is anchored on a park bench enjoying the show. He's decked out in ironed crisp, cuff-linked sleeves beneath a perfectly tailored 3-piece Italian suit. Fingering the insignia on his tweed Gatsby cap, he turns a Wall St. Journal page and lets out a breathy sigh. As I turn to go back towards the hotel, he smiles my way and shakes his head making eye contact.

"Be careful young man."

A panorama of gray clouds parting, the fading sun peeks through and reflects off a silver mirror medallion he's wearing, blinding me for a moment. As he looks across the horizon in deep thought, it feels like there's something very familiar about him.
A feminist spy?
A muckraking journalist?
Or just a crazy old uncle in the attic?

"*Nichevo*," he adds (it's nothing).
He waves his hand dismissing the conversation, waggling his furry eyebrows.

"Whatever, Pops."

7.
GOOD EVENING MR. BOND

Back up to the room. Fresh from a quick shower and decked out in Bondish styling threads, I hustle back downstairs for the next round of hedonistic depravity. My Moscow business partner is set to arrive for an evening of decadent debauchery, full of binge-drinking and sport-fucking. Seeing as I haven't been to Moscow in months, we'll definitely be hitting it hard, guns a-blazing.

With twenty minutes to kill, I park downstairs for a nightcap. Like all downtown Tverskaya hotels, the lobby bar is populated with a dozen hotties with wandering eyes and breasts at attention, waiting for  financing to arrive. I venture through the welcoming committee, enjoying the butt grabs and crotch strokes and winks, while dishing out a cynical grin of pure boredom. First drink is a double Kauffman Vodka Redbull. It lasts five seconds. Second drink meets the same fate. The third is held. The bar is packed with a decent crew of cougars-in-training, oozing hormones and charisma. I nibble on a couple babes, practicing my Russian while they practice their English, and tilt the tall glass back.

One hottie looking delicious in her slut gear, sits facing me with her legs mildly parted so I can peek up her skirt, exposing a very ripe bald cookie. Here kitty, kitty.

Out of the bathroom a spicy *dyevushka* emerges with smoky greenish-gray eyes and a coal black mane of hair, strutting towards me like a black panther eyeing up a kill. I tilt the head and smirk, looking away pretending to be unimpressed. She rests her body against mine, and sort of honks, while rescuing her wine glass from the bar.

Long pause.

She smiles. I smile.

She honks. I smile and say "nice to meet me, do I come here often?", while picturing her under a cascading tropical waterfall, peering back at me holding a remote, some anal lube, and the 7/32 wrench I lost rebuilding a 'Vette engine in the 90's.

She pulls out a piece of paper from her purse and hands it to me.

It reads *$200 for Sex*.

Ah, she's a mute....that explains the honking.

An interesting proposition. There's great potential for drinking games here. Maybe I can get her to do impersonations; starting with say Road Runner from Wile E. Coyote, then do a '57 Chevy, and maybe take a stab at the USS Reagan's throaty foghorn.

Pondering the dilemma, the eyes scan her rack falling out of her top and down her skintight miniskirt, checking out her long caramel wheels. Her face goes flush with a warm glow as she savors the attention, squinting her cat eyes at me. Tasty stuff.

Decisions, decisions. A statuesque hott with a killer body; very worthy of a test drive. But the opportunity raises questions. Once we're in the room, what kind of music do I play? How can I tell if she orgasms? Do I need a clown's horn to honk back at her? Nah, too much work. I smile and take my drink to the front desk to flirt with the girls.

After several rounds of sexual innuendos and room service sex requests, they confide to me that mute-woman is the sister of an ex-squeeze of mine. Hmmm. Sounds like trouble. The drink is killed, so I head outside to await my flashy wingman.

Off in the distance, the old coot is sitting tall, nestled on the park bench holding court with the sexy mute girl. Sumbitch. The hottie is doubled over laughing as he looks at me and flashes some sign language to her.

He sees me and calls me over.

"So do you sign to her in Russian, gramps?"

He gives me a condescending paternal head bob.

"Signing is a universal language. Pray tell young man, what possesses you to walk away from this fine elegant statue. Ivanka's taken a liking to you, and she's a tad offended. Rest assured, she's one of the most desired women at this fine establishment."

He speaks with flourished rolls of the tongue, pronouncing the words with an orator's precise enunciation; like William F. Buckley reminiscing about sneaking up and doing a stand-up doggy with a Hampton's socialite in a pleated skirt, while dining on Grey Poupon.

"If I didn't know better, I'd think you were her pimp. So, what did you just sign to her that made her laugh so hard?"

"I said you have a 3 incher and can't get it up."

He starts guffawing, wheezing, and coughing out of control.

I back away to avoid getting sprayed. Round one goes to Grandpa.

"Nice one, gramps. Don't die on me now. As much as I'd love to waste even more time chatting, I'm afraid I must bid you ladies adieu. Old Wanker, Honker. A pleasant evening to you."

"Be careful young man" with a guffaw and hack spray.

I click my heels and hustle over to the taxi stand for medical reasons.

If the old guy keels over, it may take a while for me to find someone to give him CPR.

- - -

Standing outside the front of the hotel, the hairs on the back of the neck rise, like they always do on the first night of a trip. No matter how many times I rape and pillage this city, the thrill of hunting a new batch of models makes it feel like the first time.

A lazy half moon appears long before the sun parts his shift, bringing his angry icy gusts and attitude. People switch gears from strolling to power walking, to keep the blood flowing. Their conversations paint  the horizon with little cold breath clouds like cartoon bubbles. Crisscrossing the skyline are massive creaking construction cranes, the chilly breeze amplifying their metal arms bending and twisting in piercing stubborn protests.

"So, we gonna sit here licking our balls, or go bang some bitches Snoop Doggiestyle?"

Brett welcomes the cool air for the view, as the sidewalk populates with nipple popping *dyevuskas,* working their patented nympho strut towards the nearest happy hour. Off in the distance, the aged old news 26 yr. old MILFS head for the lonely Metro ride back to the provinces, arriving just in time to catch unemployed Boris the wife beater banging the babysitter.

- - -

My Russian *mobilniki* rings like clockwork. At exactly 10:20pm as planned. The conversation is swift. It's my local connection who's been an investment partner for years. He loves his tight schedules and precise planning. Viktor is a rising star in Russia's underworld and well-connected business elite; a streetwise ideological gangster. He's in-your-face rich, mysterious, has energy to burn, and like Brett, is a terminally insane consumer of new pussy.

He rolls with the oligarch fast money players in town, and has it all going on. A contagious Russian gene. This brief Moscow debacle is being financed by a cashed up associate of his, who wants in as an additional credit line in our investment partnership. Tomorrow, we lay out the business proposal at 5:25pm sharp.

- - -

In the distance, I hear the throbbing sounds of gluttonous eccentricity. Obnoxious. Thunderous. It's a man in a hurry, racing his Big Boy Toy and pissing off as many people as he can. *Nice*. Tires screeching while asphalt melts, the car barely hugging the pavement, and then the unmistakable throaty growl of a 12 cylinder engine busting torque with fury. The beast is roaring, sprinting on its hind legs.

A black Aston Martin DB9 barrels down a side street, executing a hair-raising Jeff Gordon sliding turn, and then swerves half-cocked into an open space under my canopy. It squeals to a halt in a smoky haze of vaporizing rubber. The door opens, and out pops Viktor, make that virtually catapulted out by seven hundred watts of *Down with the Sickness* by Disturbed.

"Brett, joo look like sheet!" squeezing my hand like a vise.

"Coming from you Viktor, I consider that a compliment." The crazy fuck could be my twin brother at times.

"My man, listen to deez beast. New pistons, new throaty exhaust tips, new steroid chip…I mean even though eetz mine, eet still takes my breath away."

"You going to drive this thing, or put a dress on it?"

"Da! Get in. Veer on tight schedule. So who's dee hottie with the black hair waving at joo from zee bench?"

"Some cute mute from the hotel lobby bar. I boned her sister last year, who by contrast would never shut the hell up. If I was drunk enough I'd pump the cute mute, but then I'd have to break her fingers so she doesn't tell her sister." A round of laughs as Viktor cracks open the cooler and hands me a Carlsberg.

"Brett; I think I'd prefer *dyevs* to be mute. Dey have Ferrari for a mouth and Volkswagen for a brain. So tell me, how did eet go down?"

"She walked up to me with a napkin that says "$200 for Sex.""

"Vot did joo tell her?"

"Urrrgghrrruughrrruughhhgg."

Piercing laser blue fog lamps guide the beastly sports car, which swerves like an ambulance across multiple lanes. Ignoring the horns and middle fingers, Viktor drives like a maniac, even by Moscow standards.

"Brett, before we talk beeziness, vott vas da official time?"

"According to the judges; I clocked an official hummer time of 5 hours and 19 minutes after landing," replying in my best sheepish voice, knowing how he savors this moment.

"Geez my man, my grandfather's quicker than joo. Get your priorities straight. Less passion, more aggression, Brett! Always remember. There are no ladies in Russia. They're all whores. If you want to hang with me, I vant joo under 4 hours! Gives us much more time to be shitfaced gigolos in da strip clubs!"

Shaking my head like a dejected father, I counsel the boy.

"Sorry Viktor, the lecture has lost its magic."

"Vot? Did I rush da delivery again? Damn. I thought I vaz on a roll dere; I really felt der power on da last sentence."

"That's makes one of us. No dynamics. Where's the emotion? So bitch, you got some Prime Trim lined up for tonight?"

"Da. Enough to make Roman orgy look like Sunday school."

Knowing Viktor, that's not an exaggeration.

"Hey, do you still have that bag I gave you?"

"Da, eetz in da trunk. You got clipped already?" (Cop extortion)

"Like clockwork."

- - -

Viktor has Kremlin police connections, and acquired a genuine "*ksiva*," (police ID), which technically means he's an undercover agent. He's got special plates, a siren, the flashing blue lights, we can drink heavily while driving obscenely fast around roadblocks, and not worry about the constant hassle of cops looking for bribes. We go whipping the wrong way down one-way streets while chugging vodka and the cops practically salute him. It rocks. He always keeps a packed cooler in the backseat. I dive in and corral us a second round of beers, and Snow Queen vodka. He pulls out two chilled tall flutes from the air-conditioned center console, and a 2 gram one-hitter vial of pure blow which we devour in minutes like candy. Moscow nightlife is very centralized, so we normally cab it around town during the hunt. But tonight our destination is an upscale full-service brothel several miles away from the outer concentric circle that surround the city. Most people take the Metro, which you must experience. They have elaborate designs; huge curved-ceiling halls, wide marble stairs, large bronze statues of revolutionary and military figures, mosaics depicting battle scenes and other key moments in history. There's chandelier and surrealistic art reminiscent of the halls of a European castle. Almost entirely underground, the Metro cars run every 90 seconds. A word of caution: never *ever* take it during rush hour; it's the worst claustrophobic experience you can imagine. As far as the evenings, the last train is at 1:00 am, and it's packed.

The underground escalators to the metro from street level seem like they're a mile long. It's a great ride for those lazy afternoons of drinking moonshine while shooting granny upskirts.

Viktor and I choose to take the scenic route to catch up a bit on beeziness and poon tales, working our way towards the brothel. As we're pulling up the line of taxis towards the valet stand, I'll be damned if I don't see a cab with the license plate A009DS, as in **A** (009) **D**ick **S**moker. The skeezemaster from this afternoon.

"Viktor, park at the back of the cabs and pop the trunk."

"Dat was quick, nice call."

After getting popped so much, in his trunk I keep a bag that is filled with three foot bumper stickers that I had specially made by a commercial airplane sign shop. These things have some kind of NASA adhesive for backing. Even with a blowtorch you can't get them off once they're on. I snag one and grab a squeegee, and sneak up to the trunk of the Volga taxi and quickly glue the three foot by four inch bumper sticker across the entire trunk lid.

"I love this stuff, Brett" Viktor shaking his head, as we drive past admiring my handiwork and valet park. From now on, when traffic approaches that weasel's cab, they will read in huge bold letters "Cum see me at anal-granny-fucker.com"

It's the little things in life.

Time for some Animal House drinking.

8.
ALCOHOLOCAUST
AT THE
BELY MEDVED BROTHEL

Address: Prospect Mira, 116a – Moscow **Telephone:** (495) - 687-58-22
Cover: $ 35 – no cover before 21.00
Private Dance: $40 a song, $ 115+ for three songs!
Private Room: $ 58/hour
Website: http://www.berloga.ru

(Note: If using the metro, take the orange line to Alexseevskaya, which is just 2 stops beyond Prospect Mira. The club is right on Prospect Mira, about 100 meters from the Metro station. The entrance sign to the club is a big Polar Bear.)

Moscow has evolved into the world's capital of bling, and of the 60 odd strip clubs, **Bely Medved** is the kingpin for gold-plated sleaze. This is upscale Moscow, an elitny breed of drunken eroticism abused heavily by the mega-rich oligarchs and corporate credit card commandos. A flashy Vegas-like showcase club, stuffed with OMG sexy lean dancers who perform elaborate choreographed acts. Serious athletic talent by smoking hot pole dancers. Forget the lame stripper shuffle. These are scantily clad scorchers whipping out shows from erotic to Cirque du Soleil.

Layout:
Sky-high ceilings with an elevated circular stage front and center. Full-blown light show with crisp, booming cheesy tunes, mirror ball with a laser show. Multi-story pedestal side stages with non-stop topless grindage downstairs, and nude upstairs. Serious eye candy, with ten girls going at it at once.

Circling the dance floor is levels of coliseum seating; tiers of cushy fondle booths in cozy nooks with an unobstructed view of the whole club. Upstairs has nude dancing in dimly lit couch areas, and close encounters are to be had in mirrored *pozhaluistas* (private rooms). The private room's décor is a low slung circular couch at the base of a mini-stage with a stripper pole. If you have a vibe going, occasional freebies can be had. Otherwise, expensive pay for play if they're attracted or you're rich. Gold plated wallets are encouraged.

Clientele is rich expats, corporate horn dogs, young trust fund drunks, and it's classy enough that men even bring dates. The dark cubbyholes are often full of wealthy gangsters. In the interest of self-preservation, try to keep your eyes to yourself.

Viktor is a regular here, and skates us through the Face Kontrol goons. The door girls pipe up quickly looking for after hours work. We grin, rate, and ignore them. Enter stage right. As always, the crop is extremely ripe tonight. Instant blonde-arushki wood. While the tens are usually scooped up solving world peace in the private rooms, there are plenty of face melting scorchers working the pussy terrain.

Stupid money rules the night here. $115 lap dances (wallet dances), which are sold in 3 song groupings. ("No thanks, but can you get me an $80 beer?") If you're a drunken newbie, you could easily toss out your AMEX and end up a grand lighter, with nothing to show for it but blue balls. Directions to the shitter is $18.

A flurry of flesh dashes in my peripheral vision. I sneak a casual peek into the gangster gazillionaire territory. A pile of hotties are mauling a guy, who's laughing and groping and spanking the night away. In the midst of his belly rolls we hear "I am very little man, but I have zee very beeg power."

He probably owns a Casino, a few brothels, a counterfeit beluga caviar distributorship, and half a dozen restaurants. And half a dozen police chiefs. His sole contribution to this visual is a rising circular cigar plume from his mega-bling hand, decked out with a diamond encrusted Rolex, massive pinky ring and thumb toupee. The table is crammed with empty shot glasses and bottles and hormones and panties. I observe his inventory with an envious smile. His taste is impeccable. His portfolio of sculptured, curvy amazons is prime sirloin.

V iktor elbows me. On our right, taking in the floor show are an anorexic German and his jealous beefy wife, sitting miles apart in a booth. Quite the couple, going for that pencil neck geek hooks up with enraged wooly mammoth vibe. AIDS skinny Egbert is beaming ear to ear, having won the Moscow trip selling Encyclopedias door to door. Having been starved of that thing we call lust for several decades, this is his big moment, and he's living large!  (while sipping a $12 soda). The last daring thing they did as a couple was twenty years ago, dancing the Macarena at Aunt Gertrude's wedding.

The guy is a total tool, with barely enough 'tude to get kicked out of a Hannah Montana concert. Behind Marty Feldman bulging eyes, he's like totally mesmerized by like the slithering pole dancers and like the nudity and stuff. Drool balances precariously on the edge of his quivering lip, with a hint of Girl Scout tears in his tweedledick eyes. Huffing and puffing, it's clearly been eons since he's seen a hard body, as his frenzied speed clapping has left him with raw, bleeding stumps.

Cause that's how he likes to roll.

Hottie wife Helga has the IQ of a potato, smells like a Mardi Gras piss trough, and is predictably bored. And frumpy. And built like a middle linebacker at a small mid-western college. Her sheer girth in such hallowed coochie grounds like this reeks of industrial-strength audacity and wrongness. In protest, her huge racing-striped granny boxers have purged a green heated Hiroshima cloud hovering above their booth.

As her demands to leave go unanswered, steam explodes out her ears like a scalding teapot kettle. And that purring lovey dovey wifey voice rises in a shrill crescendo at Egbert, its sound like a shovel scraping cement. She's deeply offended to be parked in this dark pit of sin, mingling amongst the souls of the wretched.

"You'll pay for this. Oh, *YES* you will!," she sniffs snootily.

Probably with his tongue rammed up her Never Neverland.

But for now she's more entertained scratching the hairy pimples on the saggy flesh weights around her cankles, while gnawing on the edge of the end table, working on that challenging third chin. The night was not a total loss, though. A waiter helped relieve her of a chronic pain in her left side. Lifting several Michelin rolls of stomach lard, he cleaned out the troubled area with a rag soaked in gasoline, when low an behold…out popped the remote control they lost two years ago…and 37 cents in change.

Here's your effin' tip, you ssscchh-vv-vine!

She caresses the favorites button on the controller, dreaming of being transported home to watch late night cable fishing.

-   -   -

O n our left is a Gen X Moscow mutant of trust fund genes, with an epic Neanderthal brow ridge over his eyes so deeply set, they look like hollow sockets. Hovering high above is a Vanilla Ice hairdo that's so tall, sculptured and thick you could take sand wedge divots and snugly park a liter Stein. Above his army tags and greasy chin pubes, he has that laughably naïve look, convinced he's gaming hott Nikkol on his lap, she of the soft and juicy can-cans and finger-licking thighs.

Poor Sergei.

This bouffant poseur is so fubar hammered, his pupils move independently of each other. His mug resembles a melting Picasso acid portrait. His sole means of anchoring her is stuffing a half-inch of rubles in her thong every few minutes. Nikkol's got big doe eyes and a sweet befuddled look, doing her painful best to dodge getting pepper-sprayed by mongo-slobber every other sentence, while pretending not to notice the vanilla shake in his crotch. I catch her attention. She rolls her eyes and winces. Stripping is a noble profession of quick decisions. Just what *is* the going rate for selling your soul and getting spit on? $200? No. $500? maybe…

The end of this charade will come swift. The decision is already made; it's just a matter of playing it out. Eventually, even his money will bore her into racing for the dressing room. She bolts. With his rendezvous with Titty bar history cut short, it leaves him doing a Hail Mary nose-dive into the carpet, clawing at her ankles and humping her leg like a windup poodle. In an hour he'll be home yanking it like a safari park chimp. Or maybe she just left to get a raincoat.

Working the perimeter, Viktor and I flirt our way down a chorus line of strippers against the crushed velvet walls, like a 3D Vargas painting. Nipples and navels whisper approval back with each lurid sexual innuendo. When two hotts start mauling my package, my shoes come screeching to a halt. Taking control of the situation, Commander Viktor of the Death Vodka Attack Fleet bolts to acquire liquid ammunition and set up base camp. During his route, he harpoons a few stray alcoholic blonde amazons looking to guzzle free shots in return for sniffing our crotch.

As for King Brett back at Tinkerbell row, I bob and weave and peck and fondle the high-heeled wall flower babes, like Larry Flynt after a case of scotch at a High School freshman social.

The 1st girl has cool sophisticated blue eyes.
The 2nd's eyes…a rare shade of exotic green.
The 3rd's rotate inward; Diamonds – Cherries – Rubles – Vodka.
The 4th's I never did catch…

…she's spun her gorgeous gymnast body around and bent over, presenting her ass to me like a handshake from Satan. The baby soft curves of her curvaceous sculptured bootie are pure Michelangelo.

A holy Temple of Worship.

Turning around she stops me in my tracks with a sloppy kiss, sucking on my tongue seeking temporary employment as an oral assistant. My hands perform unsanitized filthy maneuvers on her innocent body, while my mouth makes astonishingly absurd promises of Ft. Knox Gold transfers to her thong, which we both know are preposterous.

Well, at least one of us does.

"Joo private room me now?"
  Smirk. Eyebrow raise.
"Joo remembers me next time joo come club, Da?"
"Honey, I won't remember you in thirty seconds."

Still a six or two low, Brett needs some serious drinking to start working the magic. Fortunately, my running mate Viktor is a bottomless liquor pit and lecherous sex fiend like myself. We're perfect wingmen. No cockblocking egos or attitudes. Simply competitive pussy wranglers in the hunt, with a passion for life bathed in illusion. In this sport, when you're overseas and have game and money, the kill is guaranteed. It's the chase that the stories are made of.

Viktor has corralled three gorgeous strippers and is dialed in, covered head to toe in a juicy trifecta of bald tacos. Our location is prime. He snagged a few dimly lit love seat booths in the secluded, dark pit in the back, which we've affectionately dubbed pervert row. We get away with so much filth back here, it would embarrass a necrophiliac pedophile caught sodomizing a nun. I sweep the perimeter, and give him the *order enough liquor for a parched Iraq softball team* look.

Time to skate a stealthy five minute lap through the levels of the club, eyeing all the available meat like a nymphomaniac butcher. In Strip Clubs, I always stand until I choose my prime targets. There's nothing worse than sitting down and swatting away the C team the whole night, while they launch guilt trips on you. After memorizing the features of my favorite top prospects, I head back and park it. The table has a line of shots, buckets of beer, and blonde racks falling out of their straps.

  Home at last. We clink drinks.

  "And so it begins, Viktor."

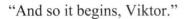

As it's the first night in town for me, I start inhaling liquor at a pace worthy of medical journals. When I'm on a business vacation, it never occurs to me that catchy phrases like *Drink Canada Dry* are a slogan, and not a personal challenge. We spend an hour or so getting blitzed, and getting to know the inner parts of our dates. Viktor passes around 5 one-hitter vials of coke, which makes the pace of comedy flow at a feverish pace. He's already bonked at least two of hotts, so there's no dance pressure. Three educated babes oozing with sexual charisma, who will meet after work if we want.

"So Brett, Viktor say joo are expert on da Russian cultural experience. Deez true it eez?" asks one of the hotts.

Oh oh, I gave the boy five minutes. Judging by his shitty grin, there's no telling what tales he's spun, or damage he's done. I'll have to test the waters and straighten the girls out quick.

"While it's true I'm a voracious connoisseur of the Mariinsky Imperial ballet, the Moscow Philharmonic and the Bolshoi Theatre, my first love has always been a sloppy Bely Medved blowjob."

"So how Moscovites artistic tastes compare to da Vest Side of New York, say da Broadway Theatre district?"

"Hello? Is this thing on?" smacking the beer bottle microphone.

"So which one of you girls licks pussy the best?" not about to let them steer the conversation in any direction but the gutter.

"You know a threesome doesn't count unless there's some girl on girl carpet licking."

"Dat's right," Viktor chimes in. "Eetz a poosie law, duly codified and available for jour scrutinizing lens at da Moscow Institute of Lust."

Two of the girls point to the third. The hottie squirms in her seat and holds one hand high.

"Guilty as charged!" in the cutest girly-girl squeak, while tonguing her eyebrows.

"Nobody knows that better than Timex," giggles another stripper.

"Who's Timex?" I ask, while cupping the nearest ass and tilting back some vodka.

Blondie pulls her thong aside, exposing slippery pink lips.

"Timex…she takes a licking, and keeps on ticking."

"Brett….Viktor says joo famous pornstar, and lick better than any girl. He sez joo have tongue like serpent, and go for dayz" Ivanka coos, her eyes bright enough to light the Kremlin basement for a week. She blows a kiss, uncrosses her legs and gives me a whiff.

"True honey, but didn't he tell you? Today is a pussy holiday for Americans."

Brett doesn't lick the help in strip clubs.

My eagle eyes pan the stage and the perimeter of the club, as my three favorites haven't made the lap by us yet. My technique here, like all titty bars worldwide is no dances. I want the sure thing, and only with a girl who meets my criteria. Young, damn near perfect ten body, dirty knees, lack of self-respect, your basic giggling drunk nympho with an IQ of 10. Like any cultured expert.

Tonight's goal is either hooking up at my hotel after work, arrange a daytime excursion, or private room full contact sessions. Viktor and I always get what we want; it just comes down to patience and selection.

- - -

My crotch sword senses a hottie and starts banging his head on my zipper. Sure enough, a fresh contestant is eyeing me from ten feet. A short, ripped denim skirt hovers top thigh above lean sleek legs in need of a thirsty tongue. A sheer laced fingerless glove on the

right hand lends some style to sleaze. She's a ripe textured spinner anxious to impale herself on me, with a high and tight bootie you could rest a surf and turf combo platter on... and still have room for a pony keg. Her bright green eyes have that naughty gaze, looking quite at home in our private lust dungeon in the back of the club. I feel a possible love connection. She flashes an erotic charge between my wallet and her eyes.

Exotic. Porn. Star.

In. Training.

Just as she's about to make her move, a tenured aged MILF of 26 years cuts in front and pussy-blocks her. Granny's skin is weathering rather elegantly like an old leather jacket, as she trolls for drunk newbies, armed with a potpourri of mind fucks and assorted wallet vacuuming tricks. Clearly she's at the wrong table. She pretends returning imaginary eye contact thinking:

"Oh yeah, they're good-looking and horny for my stuff, and rent is due, and I need free drinks, and I can't believe I just gave my cell to that Goodyear blimp pretending to be cashed up..."

I peer over the shoulder of the invisible Jurassic Park Cougar at ESPN on the plasma, thinking Shaq has transformed into an old school Fat Albert cartoon thug who can't even hit the side of a barn. Imagine if he showed up at your house and asked to borrow the shitter.

The young little bundle of hotness pushes the MILF aside, dodging the gray hairs and flying cellulite. She makes her move. As she skates her way over in a hurry, I have to cover my mouth from laughing. The strut is all wrong - clearly a virgin to those absurd two-story stripper heels. With bodacious cartoon-sized tatas you could ski down, she wobbles towards me in a cockeyed forward pitched angle.

She walks like a T Rex with a monster boob job.

I sit firm and protect my turf, a horny Raptor with happy fondle paws, and a spunky greasy bone in my lap aching to get gnawed on. She parks her gym rat arse on my lap, smelling like sweat, rank perfume, and an unmistakable mood killer scent. In life, there are two things that smell like fish. One of them is fish.

. . . sniff, sniff . . .Egads. Me head a splode!

Viktor peeks over a stripper shoulder at my chick. With frantic eyes and the slashing neck signal, he gives the Def Con 5 look. You remember that look; that same fear in the eyes you saw from your grandmother at age 14, when she caught in the last row at church with a jar of Vaseline and your pants down, eyeing the Zimbabwe tribal boobs section of National Geographic.

Holding my breath, I grin ear to ear and wait to see why the lousy rating. It takes all of five seconds. Ms. Amateur teenie blows it and goes all business on me. First sentence she offers $200 for a half hour of dancing, like that's some bargain, and then launches into a sob story about her poor mother, drunk dad, Chernobyl sister, and laundry list of things she needs money for. A total buzz kill.
Her woe is me tale of tears is tragic.
Enough to make kittens cry.
It moves me. Like industrial strength laxative.

It turns out she's the hottest stripper *ever*, or so I'm informed. What can I say? Unaware of her supermodel status, I've been a blind fool, living in a void. I have, in fact, cut myself repeatedly to atone for my previous naiveté. If a word here and there is misspelled, I do apologize, but this shortage of blood is making me woozy, and the only thing keeping me going is my love for this incredible woman. Surely her majestic body, and the inner depths of her soul, a soul that is the hallmark of smelly strippers with 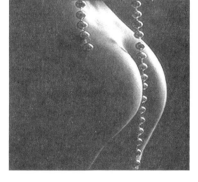 questionable drug habits, do not belong to Bely Medved, but instead to the world. Excuse me while I cry in my beer.

"Stripping eez just a job. But when I'm on stage, eetz a fine art. Joo lucky, I'm da best girl here. I like joo. Joo look like a man who can afford a woman vith my looks. My phone number is $100, and da rest vee work out at jour hotel room. So…Vee go?"

I dip my fingers in a glass of ice water and spray her.

"The power of Christ compels you…(splash)

The power of Christ compels you…."

If I had a clear view from the beginning, her story would have been obvious. In the shadows from a distance, she looked all soft focus and

perky and divine. Up close, her over-tattooed body looks like a bad crayon accident. Plus, Ms. Swampcrotch has dark shadowy circles around the eyes like a hung-over raccoon. She screams of issues; peeing in your bed, a stolen 8-ball of yay-yo, warrants, diseases, and her boyfriend Spike McPsycho in jail for raping a German Shepherd on Valentine's Day.

The ears are set to flat line, while I dodge any impression of paying attention to skunk taco. Glancing down, her 12-inch transparent platform heels contain live suckerfish swimming in them with clothespins on their nostrils.

"Good call Johnson," I yell at my dick. He shrivels up into a turtle head wailing "*YIKE. . . Yike . . . yike . . . y1ke.*"

Ms. Ivory Tower thinker keeps droning on and on, gagging and choking like a soap opera drama queen on methadone, and casually launches a sandpaper cough in my face, sensing I'm running low on tuberculosis.

Viktor holds his nose and points a finger gun to his temple…(the bastard will be dining on this story for months.)

One stripper imitates fly fishing casts. Another licks between her V-shape fingers and yells out "Joo in luck Brett. Eetz past midnight. Pussy holiday over."

Hottie spinner is a living, breathing Greek Tragedy; a perfect hard body with pink coconut-sized airbags you could feed a village with, all gone to a complete waste. In her dark future, following a short-lived mail order bride gig, a UT frat will rent her as an inflatable raft during Spring Break in South Padre.

While a plastic surgeon weeps…

Deafening silence follows. Pussy marinates. Oxygen a rare commodity. While her nuclear scent did dislodge a huge chunk of ear wax, it's so potent another minute on my leg could actually alter my DNA, if not kill me outright. I pause to choose the perfect insult, and prepare her ejection seat. I suppose I could ask her to remove her shorts and thong to revive the gagging customers. We could light a fire and toss them in and dance around the flames like wild Indians. To make things worse, she flags down a waitress, stands and starts ordering a buffet of drinks and shots….like she's setting up Camp Skunk for the evening!

I don't think so!
The waitress writes down "Sold! $80 of watered down crap."
She asks me what would I like…

"Smelling Salts!," while I dip my fingers in a pitcher of ice water and splash myself in the face…to determine if this is real or just a horrid dream.

"Oh you mean liquor? Nothing, unless she's buying. I'll be upstairs with my girlfriends in the private room. Thanks," and stuff some rubles in her healthy rack.

The waitress is a real cutie. Fresh out of the provinces, she's a slice of innocence and purity, with gobs of hormone grease on the edges. She flashes a *Welcome to my Jungle* smile and squeezes my package when I tweak her nipple. All waitresses are wannabe dancers in training, tucked away in the farm system working sausage till they get called up. The easiest lays in a club.. Like most waitresses, I'm sure in her mind she's secretly hotter than all the dancers. Well, she can certainly hold her own.

 Time to mess with stripper bitch.

 "So how long have you had a dead carp up your snatch?
 Are you still doing Donkey shows in Tijuana?"

The stripper doesn't understand my English, so she looks over at Viktor for help closing her dance pitch. Viktor's dialed in and lost for the moment in his own imaginary invisible world. One of the girls is giving him a hand job; another is straddling his lap, alternating nipples in his mouth. Every time he tries to drink his beer, she slaps it deftly aside with a perky titty. Somewhere in there is a competition to fill the 3 am slot on the 24 hour Sports Channel.

Dancer bitch turns back with her jaw dropped in a full deer in the headlights shock. Some words start spilling out of her mouth, but her face fades away, as I see one of my prime A-list candidates going up the stairs towards the VIP honey hole, decked out as the naughty schoolgirl in lace stockings and a checkered miniskirt.

A Siberian Seductress.

Looking over her shoulder, her eyes catch mine as she pauses at the top of the stairs. She does the hand to mouth BJ signal.
Ah, she's speaking my language.

The amber green and blue stage lights catch her silhouette, highlighting her golden flowing hair, mischievous personality, and long showgirl legs built for sex. The Johnson head-butts approval high on the zipper in secret hard-on code, signaling he senses a Bond girl villain in need of harpooning. He waves off command control, inserts the launch codes and instantly goes hot.

Nikkita – Russian model turned cock assassin. Meow!

Her seduction phasers on ten, she's looking to rape me and ATM me and ride me like a Rodeo Bull in heat. Sucking on her index finger, she pulls it out and beckons me with it; then flashes a nice peek-a-boo up her teenie-weenie checkered skirt. Her ass crack smiles at me. I smile back. The planets align. Time stands still…while a werewolf howls at the moon.

I must be strong. Fight this journey towards the dark path. Sure, I could ignore her advances and hide for a month in my hotel closet sucking my thumb. But that could cause turmoil in the markets. Grabbing two Heinekens, the mind goes blank, as her Blonde kryptonite overpowers me. I feel my legs pulling me towards her.

"Viktor. Ten bucks if you sniff her chair."

- - -

Like a 12th century Viking in the hunt, I march up the stairs on a rogue pilgrimage, looking to drown myself in a sea of flesh. At the turn, I pass a tiny Asian chick with the blank gaze of a Lolita staring at Saturday morning Manga cartoons, though more likely it's a seasoned glare from sitting on her knees and being painted with a gallon of silly string in one bukkake scene too many. Her lone brain wave emits a low humming noise heard only by stray alley dogs.

As I hit the top of the stairs, I do the over the shoulder stripper pose sticking my ass out at Ms. Dumpster stripper, who's leaving our table. She gives me the finger, and saunters off on a mission to con the nearest drunk mental midget into dropping his kid's college fund so he can lick the battery acid off her Mr. Ed lips.

It sucks how some pros take all the fun out of the sport. Who taught an eighteen year old such hardcore tactics? They should be flogged. SHE should be flogged.

- - -

Upstairs is all-nude, versus topless downstairs. The sexpot parks me in a dark corner, and attaches her ass to my lap like a staple gun. Her lips full and inviting, she has an infectious laugh and a glassy cackle in her eyes, and a 2000 volt sexual charisma that beckons me, like a fluff girl on scuffed knees. A certified horny Russki party chick. She gazes soulful and deep into my eyes. I gaze soulful and deep at her meat curtains peeking out the sides of her thong. Her cameltoe shrine oozes such heat; it melts the label of my beer, forcing me to break out Vaudeville skills, juggling the red hot glass while licking alternate nipples.

Hotsie McHotstuff is like a horny octopus, with warm hands everywhere stroking my stuff in every direction, her suction cup mouth feeding off my skin. Fresh off the stage, her glistening thighs of slickness beckon me to slide headfirst down them and bury my noggin' in her Venus Flytrap. As far as her upstairs goods, her fluffy Slavic pillows call for me to play celery stick bongo tunes on them and dive in for a sweaty BBrrumskki. Only the Jaws of Life could pry me away from these yummy party favors.

 Shots and stiff drinks appear quickly to speed up the speed seduction. In no time I manage to lure this ridiculously curvy Bond girl under my Jaeger bomb spell. Coolly dishing out the patented player shtick; body language leaning away, winking at other girls, acting witty, aloof and disinterested. She falls for it immediately. Although I prefer spinners, statuesque long Russian legs drive me nuts, and her glistening tan set of wheels are picture perfect.

Her tasty swelling boobage is denting out her *I Dream of Jeannie* top quite nicely, and when I open just two buttons, the firmness of her rack pops open the rest. Pink silver dollar areolas dance inches from my lips, bouncing in perfect unison with each girly giggle. Their date with slobber destiny looms. I lick my eyebrows in anticipation.

For foreplay, she does some token stripper curiosity questions, which amazingly contains words with multiple syllables. My eyes never leave her rack, while she yaks away about her fascination with all things American, with Disney World taking first place for her favorite Historical Landmark. Horny Nikkita exudes class and charm, but more importantly, she has the endearing habit of stroking her pussy between sentences. With the curious eyebrow raised, I switch on the auto-pilot and do the interested face with head nods performance, while I replay on my mental hard drive the video of me recently banging some twins on the Laquito Beach in Cartagena.

- - -

I dig *dyevs*. They speak multiple languages, are streetwise and educated, and are the polar opposites of western women. Pure femininity. No bipolar neurotic man-hating prudes. And it's not just their laughably superior looks; it's their voracious appetite  for life. It comes from the broken culture of corruption, the huge disparity of wealth, and a Russian male gene pool full of drunken women beaters. Russian women maintain the intellectual curiosity and hormones of a teenager until their late 20's. Never bitter. Always horny. Always looking to move up in life while experimenting with every self-destructive vice along the way.

There's something about a Russian girl's voice. It's like no other. A sexy high pitch. So sweet and so young and naïve sounding. It has a melody to it. When Nikkita talks, it seems as if honey is falling off her words. I leave her plenty of room to babble away, selling herself to me, while I affectionately stroke her cookie like a college professor altering an F. The girl is flat out sexy and contagious. Her life's story lacks that little thing called direction, but she is in no hurry to get there. She lives for the moment. We slide lower and lower in the booth, and she climbs on top of me and gives me a toe-curling tongue assault, while fondling in all the right areas. It's a hardcore sales approach, but me thinks she's closed the deal. Things accelerate in our love den.

A topless waitress with an hourglass body of tongue-lapping goodness descends from high above us with a tray full of shots and Kauffman double vodka Red Bulls. The vision as she reaches down is like the hand of God presenting lusty aphrodisiac fuel. The dancer is licking her lips and rubbing my Johnson back and forth - maybe she's making a wish? The waitress giggles and begs for her to pull my tool out so she can hop on it. We are in a dark secluded area, but that's a tad much. But not to be rude to a lady, I let the dancer pull it out, and  the waitress bends over and bobs up and down a bit, finishing with a lengthy soul kiss. When she finishes, I ask for a tip.

"So vat is it you do?" dancer babe slurs with a curious glance, while doing a slow pump of the package.

"In the daytime, I'm a barely legal porn couch auditioner. At night I suppose you could consider me a performance artist."

"Hummpf. Artist. A painter. Dat's goud. Really fookin' goud. Vat style joo eez? Vat is it joo draw best?'

"I specialize in painting thick white lines from the crack of the ass to the base of the neck."

"Dat goud. I like dees, jess. But really, I always vanted to paint. Dat's probably sound stupidz, no?"

"Yes. It sounds very stupid."

-    -   -

More Jaegerbombs, double vodka Red Bulls and tequila shots get inhaled like it's a fraternity last call in New Orleans on Fat Tuesday. Nikkita's naked now, saddled up riding a finger, while molesting me in a feeding frenzy. Despite the booming sub-woofers and sweeping greenish-purple strobe lights, one booth over contains two freshman Kamikaze Komrades. They've passed out with playing cards in their hands, their shoes caked in globs of *pivo* and peppermint schnapps.

BapMan #1 has a melted face, like he looked too long at the Arc of the Covenant. He's a fine tuned pussy magnet, going for that puke frozen mid-swoop between lower lip and keg belly look that chicks go nuts over. His partner, Boris Upchuck is cartoon massive, with huge hands and bulging arms; in the middle of his Gigantor shoulders sits a tiny shaved head with earrings; the mysterious love child of a cue ball and Mr. Clean.

It's all about pace, guys.

- - -

Back in the booth, my stripper gets the token twenty-second neck and back rub with one hand, while a wandering finger buries deep into her warm honey hole. It's all sweet smelling and pure, like a Navy Seal's armpits on a weekend furlough in Bangkok. She runs her fingers through my hair and asks for more details about my life.

With 10,000 hours of time tested strip club repertoire, Brett is seasoned wordsmith spinning sarcastic tales of intrigue and humor like a phrase fencing master. . . the BS flows like chilled brandy, sprinkled with a smorgasbord of irrelevant facts and fiction, and painted thick with sexual innuendos and insults that fly over her head like a strip club flyer in the breeze. She crawls all over me wanting more, her manicured claws digging into my back. Then again, I'm willing to pay, so the rap elevates to stratospheric levels instantly.

The rap goes perfect, and she asks to come over after work and spend tomorrow afternoon with me. (I could take her tonight, but then I'd have to pay the club $500 and still have to pay the girl). In a hurry and hammered, I want in-house service, so I hesitate and frown in silence. Pretend to be a confused amateur. Horny and on a mission, she puts her fingers on my lips and demands we go to the *Komhata* (private sex room) for a fuck fest immediately. No money, all honey. (girls who say this still expect a big tip, but say it as a compliment).
   "Joo and I naked togezher, everyzeeng eez pozeeble !"

As she stands up, she turns an ankle on those circus high heels and bites the turf hard, looking like a bass flopping around in the bottom of the boat as she attempts to become upright.
   If there was ever a mating signal…Check mate!

I shell out a Benjamin for one hour in a *Komhata*. When you know the outcome going into the room, inside the girl takes on a new level of sexiness in your eyes. The heart races. Chills battle goose bumps.

She wastes no time on the little stripper stage they have in there; just sinks to her knees, rips my pants down and cups my ass with both hands, parting her swollen lips. Still standing, I strap myself into the convenient parachute straps hanging from the ceiling. I place my shoes snugly in the track starting blocks, and assume the speed hummer position. One hand holds a beer, the other fists her hair. The gun goes off, and I instantly ram it hard in and out of her mouth, holding a boxing match with her tonsils and cheeks, denting the back of her throat. When I pull out unexpectedly and slap her in the face with it, she tries to latch on and suckle it like a pacifier.

Nice try sister. I respond by plunging back in for deeper throat action, which fills the air with those romantic throat gurgles and choking noises full of slobber, fear and lust.

It's an East/West conflict of the ages; the West is holding territory with aggression and liquored fury, while the East seems to be going down for the count.

Party girls join us on the stage

Like all dyevs, she's got Jenna J. genes, the natural porn instincts that makes your nuts tighten and toes curl. Why the beast treatment? Brett learned years ago, polite will get you nowhere in bed with a Russian girl. They have zero respect for the Casanova singing *Dahwling, I vant to make love to you.*

If the sex was at her apartment, on the way out I'd kidney punch her kittens and pee on the family photo…and she'd orgasm watching it. A great session. One of the most aggressive BJs I've had in a long time; I mean in at least 4 hours.

The chick sucks it like she just got out of prison, so fast and deep my balls are slapping against her chin. As expected, in the middle of it the horny waitress pops in to watch, while pretending to take drink orders. She seems quite happy to chit chat about Grandma's cookies and competitive basket weaving while Deep Throat 12 is being filmed in front of her. I yank her over and plant a wet one on her.

Soon I hear the textbook Russian mating call: "*I vant fuck now!*" When I flip Nikkita over on all fours, there's a tattoo on her ass that says "If you can read this, please do a reach around and fondle my clitoris." The bonking is borderline record material as well, with the hottie riding me six ways to Sunday. If there are 16 muscles in the snapper, this girl could constrict all 17 of them. I feel like I'm being gripped by a slippery wet pink vise and she loves every filthy second of it….dishing out a raw guttural noise.

Yelling. Screaming. Moaning.

Oozing coochie juice drips down her thighs as she cries in a state of rapture. Her performance is awe inspiring, at least worthy of a runner up for the Academy Award for its authenticity. She could just be a great actress, but like all stallions, I refuse to believe it was anything less than the greatest lay of her life.

Why do woman fake their orgasms?

Because they think men care.

Session over. Drinks get chugged. Clothes get put on. She gives me her phone number and asks to come over after work, no money requested. I palm a healthy tip in her hand.

"Be careful young lady."

-   -   -

As we leave the private room, she pushes me against the door and smothers me one last kiss.

Slow and sensual. Like old lovers.

Ouch. I'm going to remember this one. She's something special. This girl could really do some damage to my heart, if I wasn't a twisted binge-drinking nymphomaniac living above a strip club in Asia.

And as she heads back downstairs to dance her next set, a thousand miles away a malnourished priest strolls through the desolate fields of Siberia counseling his disciples saying "you never know how sweet the apple is until you reach the core."

I find comfort in these wise words. And as I watch the perfect contours of her bouncing bubblebutt slither away, I wonder if she to finds consolation in their meaning. Does she battle her own demons? Were their moans actually tribal incantations? Or does it all get lost in translation, and leave her tragically having to settle for a few orgasms, some cash, and a puddle of smiling sweat.

But then again, there are no apples in Siberia, so the priest may not have been speaking from personal experiences.

-   -   -

Time to move back towards Camp Viktor. As I approach the top of the stairs, a smoking hot Black chick stops me and gives me the once over, purring in that South African accent I absolutely love. Highly cultured English phrasings with gigantic, fabulous, impossibly massive adjectives, coupled with smooth sophistication. For phone sex, she could read me the dictionary and I'd get a hard-on.

Seeing as I just finished a session, I'm not in play. But to be honest, despite her tear jerking banging body with a curvy back, the most perfectest bootie ever, and smooth world class thighs that would break me in half, she is friggin' huge….I mean Jolly Green Giant tall.

I'd need a ladder just to talk to her nipples. Sensing this, she insists on putting her rock hard titties in my face…yummy milk helmets…I mean magnificent, scrumptious, mouth-watering milk helmets with Hershey kisses nipples bathed in an autumn scent of orange mango, and well… my crotch-breath.

-   -   -

Running towards the stairs is a squat Russki in Herman Munster elevator shoes. Fresh from the Denny's buffet, he's out to slay women with his patented killer shtick and GQ Wal Mart playa looks.

He whips up the stairs on a mission to fondle Pornella Gigantress. What in the world is he thinking? I'd tell him to stand up, but he already is. This must be some urgent space time/height continuum barrier he must cross.

"We represent, the Lollipop Guild, the Lollipop Guild" chants the Johnson.

Got to give him props for his all-out effort. Decked out in a leopard print Flintstone one piece, he's put dinner plates in his lips and starts bustin' Tupac raps. He raises his war painted arm, and launches a spear some 50 yards across the dance floor below, nailing a spotlight like a coconut. Sheena is unimpressed, and swats him away like a swamp mosquito. Adjusting the massive straw basket of fruits on his head, midget man flashes the A'ight, wat up yo yo boyz signal looking for cred, and gets shot down again. He spots me enjoying his performance.

"Dude man, can you hook a brother up with directions to the john?" he asks, adjusting the sock in his crotch.
"Follow the Yellow Brick Road."

Da cell rings…his Mom wants her car back, so he gotz ta jet. Hustling past center stage, he distributes ceremonial fruits to the dancers from the basket on his head, and exits the club in a huff. On his way to the car, he tries to steal a purse from a little old lady in a dark alley for pocket change, and promptly gets his ass kicked.

Countess Chocula's muscular arm yanks me over like a stage hook, her tire tube lips coaxing me to sample her stuff. I politely decline, while over her shoulder watch Shaq on ESPN shoot another brick. She turns around and bends over and asks "are you sure?"

Hot damn, sista. Freak dat bootie! Her tiny cinnabunz look like two baby seals fighting over a piece of dental floss. She stands and spins back around, my heartbeat racing while I consider subscribing to National Geographic. I hug her kneecaps, kiss her shin and wish her the best.

T ime to cart my happy ass down to the lower level. An hour of sex has left me embarrassingly behind in my drinking. Arriving back in the dark pervert row, Viktor and two blondes have fled the scene, the table is lined with dead soldiers. There's just one of the

hotties left at our table, slinkering so low in the chair she's almost falling of it. Viktor has done some serious damage while I was gone. The boy makes me proud sometimes.

She's half passed out sitting by herself, her head bobbing off her exposed rack, with her thong pulled completely to the side.

"I see Timex" says my Johnson, the Master of the Obvious pointing out her flapping bat wings. Meaty, raw and pink. Yummy. Pass me some A1 sauce.

Pretending to be a stripper, I sit sideways across her lap and ask for an $800 dance, while picturing her naked in church riding a Sybian while shot-gunning a warm 24oz. can of Schmidts. She rebounds, giggles and peers up at me with a red-eyed Alzheimer's look of love. Despite no recollection of me, she grabs a hand and slides my finger into her snapper, peering at me through swollen slits.

"Yo' Adrian, ...ya gotta cut me!" laughs the Johnson.

The girl is sorority initiation tanked.

With the table down to a few drinks, I order a Unesco beer bucket and a tray of shots and an anti-hangover pitcher of water. In between massaging her boobies, we chat it up for a bit, and get to work on our new party fuel.

On center stage, the girl I just bonked is teamed up with another hottie and putting on an amazing show of athleticism. Choreographed spins. Somersaults. Back flips. Her muscular ass winking at me, her

sinuous moves done with the grace of a gymnast. Her sexiest trick was the stripper pole climb, and then with no hands she slides upside down to the stage in slow-mo, while peeling off her clothes.

There's a birthday in the house.

Wasted stripper and I applaud, while her 38C boobies do the happy jiggle. Since she's too wasted to speak, for entertainment I make her stand topless and do jumping jacks to earn her shots. She vaguely remembers Viktor leaving with her two friends, but can't be sure. I thank her for her valiant attempts at coherent thought, while picturing her under my Jag on a sliding dolly installing chrome exhaust tips while I teabag her.

Five minutes go by, and Countess Chocula slithers on over to our table for a shot and some bootie and coochie fondling. Her chiseled body is a fantasy serving of pure chocoholic sweetness. Big shiny white teeth you want to play xylophone on, inside a mouth so huge, she could devour a water buffalo in just four bites. I'm parked deep in the loveseat, the blonde's meat purse keeping my fingers warm. Chocula straddles my legs in a wide stance above me.
Here Kitty, kitty.

Those legs -- her ripped muscular hurdler thighs reach to the sky. Dancing with her hands above her head, she looks like a tan goalpost. I catch her attention away for a moment, and crawl/run through her legs and then using my beer do the Heisman Trophy pose. Greatness unnoticed. Chocula is no pressure and all fun, and gets a big kick of standing with her cookie eyelevel. I glance up at her BJ mouth and her sexy Michelin lips. She could deep throat you and you'd barely reach inside her lower lip, just past the inflate to 38psi instructions. She grins, and sensing my weakness, turns around and presents her perfect ass again to me. Say Yes to Crack!

Stripper and I run our hands up the taut muscles of her long caramel thighs and each cup a cheek while she purrs; it looks and feels like a bronzed grapefruit. I picture her getting in doggie style position on a  bed and me saddling in from behind, hands high above my head touching the bootie, my rod hovering mid-knee. Her boyfriend must have to pole vault onto the bed and lance her like a sword. Seeing as Viktor is on a sabbatical, I ponder my options for a ride back to my hotel, while gazing in awe at her legs. Fine chiseled muscle sticks with a hint of Lamborghini DNA. With that tight gearbox between her thighs, if push comes to shove, she could easily carry me piggyback 8 miles across town in mere minutes.

Suddenly a chorus of triumphant trumpets erupts, while angels start singing in awe. A hearty Tarzan yell shatters the air as Viktor the Conqueror, with a contagious post-cunnilingus lockjaw grin, comes vaulting down the stairs on a shining white Clydesdale. Saddled up with the two butt naked blondes, his medieval Damascus sword is held high in victory.

Clearly he's had a spectacular threesome. I hoist my chalice like the Statue of Liberty out of respect. Sheena raises me high above her head in the palm of one hand, spins me in a 720, and then flips me like a discus across the room onto the back of the horse. The wingmen bring the herd back home singing 5th century Roman warrior battle hymns.

9.

TROLLING FOR GEN-X NYMPHOS
Co-starring IVANA SUCKIT

"Da! Deez is da FedEx. Vee have Vodka delivery for da Mista Brett Tate"

O ne advantage of being an obsessive-compulsive adrenaline junkie is the Doctor Jekyll - Mr. Hyde lifestyle. Daytime is the hyper competitive sports and business animal, and at night a binge-drinking nymphomaniac lunatic. Not breaking records, but most would say I've made my mark. Just ask my bondsman.

Best hangover cure in the world? Sweat. At 8 am, while the world's lazy fat fucks sleep alone after viciously wanking all night to Cosmo using tears as lubricant, I'm in the gym benching 300 pounds and on the treadmill cranking out 8 miles. No brain, no pain. Sure, I could use my powers to educate and unite the republic, but I'd rather destroy it.

Life isn't all about money and pussy. You can't leave out exercise…and delusions of grandeur, and self-destructive binge drinking orgies. Oh, and money and pussy are important too.

Like all hotel gyms, the layout is claustrophobic and blows, and designed to piss you off so much you leave in three minutes, like after your first bonk with Naomi the Yiddish slut in her parent's gold Winnebago. (*Oh my Gawd, I'm like cumming, haww haww haww*).

First up is the bench. It's a decent Universal machine cramped in a corner in front of a short row of dumbbells. I'm whipping through the pyramid sets until *that poser guy* comes in. You know, the 5'5" college steroid midget on his first roid cycle, dying to flaunt his results and take on the world, before hustling back to his day job as mop guy at the Gay Peep Show theatre.

In a typical competitive brickhead gym, 250lb. monsters with 8% body fat are a dime a dozen. They never glance at themselves in the mirror except during heavy lifts for form checks. Not *that poser guy*. He does a couple warm-up stretches, but never actually lifts. He can spend hours staring at his 165 pound frame in the mirror, doing stealthy half flexes and poses. Normally this is easily ignored, but the universal bench I'm using ends a foot from the dumbbells in front of the mirror. Every time I go to lift, he's an inch from my feet in front of the dumbbells. He pretends an intention to lift, but never actually picks any weights up. He just locks eyes on the pure perfection reflecting back at him.

"Clearly the future Ahhnnold" snickers the Johnson.

My first set, as I lift the weights I spread my feet wide, intentionally bumping his shoes. He fidgets away and goes to the water fountain. Three minutes later, as I'm about to start another set, he returns an inch from my feet. He's blowing kisses in awe of himself, practicing a facial expression for his upcoming Muscle Fitness cover, while peering over at me with a fragile optimism. Before I lean back, I tell him *do you mind* and wave the hand, so he moves away. I finish the set, leave the area and get a drink of water and come back. Now he's planted right in front of the bench posing for the mirror, and hasn't lifted a damn thing in twenty minutes. What a friggin' idiot.

"Why don't you take a picture, it will last longer" I say with heartfelt encouragement for his career.

He moves away as I settle onto the bench. While I lift, he shuffles back to the water fountain and eventually slithers out of the room.

Bench done. Next comes the running. (I run 25-40 miles a week). Treadmills suck compared to reality, but downtown Moscow has no sidewalks. Minute one, alcohol unleashes forehead sweat like an exploding fire hydrant. After thirty minutes, a river has formed and the treadmill starts floating around the room, so I use the handy incline feature and well timed leans to negotiate turns off the walls. The room reeks like the bottom of a redneck moonshine vat. Workout done, it's back to the hotel room for a shower, a gallon of ice water, and a hair of the dog bloody Mary. Noon arrives. Time to hit the streets, looking for trouble.

-   -   -

Strolling through the hotel courtyard, I glance over and there's the same stylish old coot from yesterday, in a crisp Bookster Tweed 3-piece suit with leather elbow patches, a starched sport shirt and pleated Knickerbocker trousers. The guy looks like he was air dropped from a 50's movie, trolling aimlessly for a flux capacitor. Totally out of place in Moscow, he belongs in knickers on a trotting Clydesdale circling above his trusty foxhounds while twirling his waxed handlebar mustache methodically. The kind of bloke who dines eating juicy lobster by hand, yet cuts his chocolate bars with knife and fork.

He's flipping through a copy of the London Financial Times resting on a plaid blanket on his lap, perusing stock prices through his trusty monocle. Apparently gramps is a permanent fixture here. He's holding court with a gaggle of pigeons from his hallowed perch on the park bench. Puffing on a mahogany Brigham Classic tobacco pipe, the chap is Country-squire styling, looking like a British Consulate.

"Tally-ho. I gather carousing with blondes is your sport, young man" with long, breathy pauses and wet smacking lips.

"Actually, I prefer bisexual billionaire nympho-mutes. But seeing as they're currently in short supply, I'm inclined to adapt."

He ahems a throaty chuckle. Sitting tall with legs crossed, he has a far away glance on his face, squinting at nothing in particular. With a serious mop of thick gray hair above the vest, he's got that vintage Silver Fox look.

"In my youth, I was more prone to full blooded activities. Cricket, rugby and hunting were a man's sport."

"So you prefer your hands between a man's buttocks waiting for the footie, instead of a blonde?"

"Cheerio. Actually in my earlier years I likewise dabbled with blondes. Right here in Moscow to be precise, although I imagine my evenings were a pinch more regal, over a fine bottle of wine and candlelight."

"Touché. I must say you look a bit flush this afternoon. I'm a tad concerned about your diet. Not getting enough vegetables, are you?"

"You have a keen eye. I have indeed been quite lax in that department" cleaning his monocle with an aqua silk handkerchief.

"We're all guilty. Let me ask you something Gramps…do you know what the hardest thing is about eating vegetables?"

"Pray tell. What *is* the hardest thing about eating vegetables?"

"The wheelchairs."

"Actually it may not be your diet, but a lack of exercise, pops. They say walking is quite effective for increased circulation in the advanced years. Do you ever walk in the evenings for conditioning?"

"Of course not, who would mind my beloved perch here?"

"I'd highly recommend it. Take for example my 84 year old uncle. He loves it. He started walking two years ago, and now we don't know *where* the hell he is."

"Maybe your problem is sex. It's never too late to shoot another round. Try it while you're still breathing, Scrappy. I think you're suffering from blonde withdrawals, and are a tad jealous."

"For the sake of disclosure, a cynical morsel of truth, I'll spot you that."

I wink and he points a finger gun at me with a laugh.

As I'm leaving, the sun peeks through the clouds and I go blind again from the reflection of his mirror-like medallion. A weird effect. He takes a long drag, squinting at me through cumulus clouds rising above from his seasoned tobacco pipe.

"Be careful young man. I hope you find it."

"Find what."

"Come now. Don't think an old chap can't see right through you. You have that look…you're searching for something."

"Young men have eyes to, pops. Perhaps you're projecting your desires on me."

"Ah, an intellectual gambit from a worthy adversary."

"Look Pops, while I may be a searcher, your pigeons betrayed you. One of them whispered to me you're too afraid to find what you're looking for."

"Pray tell, which one of the hairy bastards talked? I'd never confess to that" his furrowed brow wrinkling at being exposed.

"A man is only as old as the woman he feels. My advice? Keep your chin up, chase some young skirts, and never trust a fart." WTF is up with this guy?

Moscow slumbers through the morning with its mutual hangover, as the moon surrenders his shift to the sun, thoroughly unimpressed. The workout peeled off a few layers, but the jet lag will keep the spinning head fog till the afternoon. Still a tad cross-eyed ripped from the night before, I feel like a beached pirate who missed his getaway ship.

I drag my marooned ass down to the bustling streets of this Grand Imperial center of Czarist tradition. Violent dour looking men whip past speed walking while barking into cells. Taxis and Mercedes race through the streets screeching horns and swerving in packs. The world is moving way too quick this morning for my jet-lagged hangover; an anvil dropped 20 stories onto my head would ricochet unnoticed. Vodka numb to the occasional icy gusts, I leap over toxic puddles rippling with reflections of an ancient cathedral with intricate curved stained glass windows behind wrought-iron gates, huddling between enormous competing glass skyscrapers, in a jungle of giant billboard ads.

The Old cramping the style of the New.

Three centuries of architectural styles side by side: a common sight

Destination this afternoon is a snazzy local Brunch Café.

During the short walk comes the traditional pit stop at the Mom and Pop newsstand, to catch up on important current events. When I'm not hung over, I like to zip in here to inhale Redi-Whip, set off mustard packet bombs in the microwaves and run for the hills. These stores are really just fronts; they're feeding bins for career alcoholics. They disguise them by putting other crap in there, but they ain't fooling anyone. This store is dressed up quite nicely with a smorgasbord of highly flammable Vodka and assorted local liquors, Slim Jims, Cigars and chaw. Yes Sir; all the essential food groups.

Overseas, Brett's a news junkie. I'm on a strict schedule of reading at least three headlines per month, to keep me grounded. In this store, I think they sell the booze to help you survive all the mind numbing stupidity printed on front pages spanning the globe. I pass over Investor's Business Daily, London's Financial Times, and the Wall Street Journal, because I want the real meat.

The news impacting the world.

News that changes your perspective on life.

From the front Cover of People Magazine.

- - -

- **_Oprah. 200 pounds and loving it!_**
  Right. Try 230 easy! A dump she fluctuates 20 pounds.

- **_Britney flushes baby down toilet after another OD._**
  She thought it was her wedding ring! You go girl!
  All trailer skank, all the time. Did you see that spy shot of her flashing in a car? Her pussy looks 90 yrs old.

- **_Perky Suzie shares her daily abused pet story!_**
  I read these and weep for humanity. Hold me Suzie.

Skipping down the sidewalk a wiser man, I hit Tverskaya Ulitsa, Moscow's swanky cosmopolitan avenue that dates back to the 12th century. This eight-lane wide road is clogged with fearless Russian drivers, aiming to pick off the naive tourist jaywalkers like a 7/10 split. Tverskaya is Moscow's answer to Fifth Avenue. Obscenely expensive. Hip cafes, nightclubs, gourmet restaurants, tourist attractions, designer boutiques, it's all here. Outrageously priced simple lunches for $50, and a $250+ dinner with drinks is commonplace. For you fat cats, I'd recommend heading down to the Four Seasons Hotel for the "Tsar's Breakfast". Kobe beef steak, foie gras, Beluga caviar and a truffle omelet, served with champagne for a mere $750.

8-lane Tverskaya Ulitsa – heading towards the Red Square & Kremlin

Running from the Kremlin towards St. Petersburg, there's some history to this turf. Some 300 years ago, Tverskaya was a narrow avenue lined with residences of the Ultra-rich Moscovites. Mansions of decadent architecture with lavish interiors lined the city. As the communist reign took hold, the homes were seized and converted into Stalinist era monumental structures. This created the need to widen the street, to the current eight lanes. Rumor has it Soviet Engineers hoisted the structures with cranes onto giant steel balls and rolled them back, creating the mega-wide thruway. Russia became the capital of world Communism. Ownership of homes was outlawed, and the country was the epitome of cheap, state-subsidized living.

Fast forward to the recent fall of the Soviet Union and the irony is thick, as it comes full circle. Once again, these same buildings have been gobbled up by the oligarch titans as residences and investment properties. As for the old farts and penny pinchers in government subsidized apartments in these buildings, if they refuse to sell, they come home and get ringside seats to watching their buildings burn, or have a meet and greet with contract killer warnings, or have the courts seize them with bogus rulings of zoning changes. Billionaire row has been re-created at the city's premier address.

Cathedral of the Annunciation - Kremlin

- - -

As there are no pedestrian crossways, I make use of the *perekhod*, or underground walkways. These are rather ingenious means of crossing major intersections; underground pathways lined with mini-commerce centers, pharmacies, kiosks, shops, currency exchanges, as well as access to the major metro lines. They come in handy during killer snowstorms; people also utilize them as meeting places.

Coming out of the *perekhod*, I focus my travel on the small boulevards just off Tverskaya. They're great for people watching, window-shopping and hooking up. The stealthy camera and hard-on alert go to level orange, waiting for command control.

Just before I reach my café destination, I walk smack into a model oasis. Out of a swinging door from an upscale department store comes a parade of stunning mega-hotties, in a flurry of blonde hair, dancer legs to their necks, and puffy nipple high beams.

Bodies of utopian purity. Raw sex statues that argue for a better tomorrow. The air fills with a high heel staccato tap-dance and girly girl giggles as they work their stuff down the sidewalk.

Damn.
It's enough Nordic hotness to melt the frost off the beard of Alaskan crabber.

The caboose is a scorching statuesque blonde in a see-thru pink blouse, whisking by inches away in a trail of hormones, sexy scents and flirty glances. Her eyes are slits of ice blue, pools of passion that freeze me in my tracks. Straight out of the Book of Temptations, her sizzling tight derriére does the porno jiggle as she moves, just begging for me to pour honey on it and play butt bongo and dine for days, while singing Barry White ballads out of key.

Brett whips his head around towards her and locks eyes using the patented Elvis sneer, while going cross-eyed in lust for her smoking hot sculptured legs. Good lord, I'd lick NYC Subway windows and pee myself for a threesome with that fuck machine. Pulse check. Predator sweat wiped. Disengage.

As the coochie mirage vanishes down the sidewalk, I stroll down a side street off Tverskaya and reach the hippie chick café, parking myself at a favorite sidewalk table. During happy hour, this place is exploding at the seams with techno, booze, and drunk blonde gazelles dancing and peacocking under neon mood lighting. At this hour though, it's a cemetery.

-   -   -

Perfect. Brett is feeling particularly flush, and can use a little break in the action to clear the head and plot the day's festivities. While pretending to read the Moscow Times, I hide behind shades, nursing an espresso and pitcher of ice water. Even my hair looks hung over.

Curbside entertainment features a tour group of crusty uni-brow German backpackers arguing directions on their upside down Lonely Planet map, while shuffling through ankle deep green puddles full of industrial chunks. Smelling like three shades of death, their soiled baggy denims are caked in week old Munich mud, sheep sperm, and blood stains from a nose picking competition, though future emails will boast of bloody scars from battling Bosnian freedom fighters.

Toting their precious duffel bags, as the day progresses all museums and tourist attractions will be passed over in a huff due to the cover charge. Their schedule will still be full though, spending twelve hours scouring the city for a slumlord they can jew down to $8 a night for an unventilated vomit stained loft to crash in….in the middle of Chechnya gangland.

- - -

A spunky Ukrainian teen in a black leather micro-miniskirt cruises by my table trailing a scent of Esteé Lauder mixed with pot smoke. She's dishing out an impressive strut in black knee-high boots with fishnets, a tiny burgundy strapless midriff, and a leather-studded choke collar. Skating past a dozen empty tables, she circles back and parks her vivacious little ass one table across facing me.

Ambitious. Mischievous. On a mission.

Eyeing me at once with a curious raised eyebrow hovering above librarian glasses, she has an infectious smile and succulent mouth with mega-puffy curled lips just aching for a money shot.

Sort of a sexy smart-ass look. I want to spank her immediately. Correction. On second glance, make that swollen lips like a giant suckerfish.

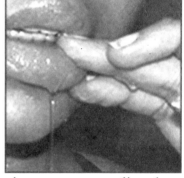

Damn.

Her mouth is wide enough to fellate a garbage can. I raise a glass in a toast.

"Nice to meet me", while picturing myself pouring a pitcher over her head and shoving a bong up her ass while she gives me a toe-curling deep throat BJ that would impress Amber Lynn.

With fire in her loins, this horny energizer bunny starts fidgeting with her Britney colored bracelets, twirling her hair and smacking her gum, while bending forward exposing some perky teen TaTas. Brett looks away incredulously bored, pretending not to notice her. It's quite the view.

"*Gentleman, start your engines*" announces the Johnson.

All she's missing is a university name tag that says *Ivana Suckit.*

Two tables over is a hilarious circus act; a pencil-neck techie geek dining with a retro-Emo fag. Making zero eye contact, geekman spends 99% of his time synchronizing his iPOD to his iPhone to his iGlasses. They're astonishingly thick coke bottle lens with a built-in GPS tracker, encrypted to pick up Satellite TV. Looking chronically constipated when he speaks, his digital obsession coupled with zero social skills creates Bizarro World bursts of geek ecstasy discoveries, followed by nuanced hyper-technical explanations that lose Emo's attention in three seconds. Then, it's back to scratching his iBalls. Where's a tire iron when you need one?

Next up is today's Darwin candidate, Emo fag. He's doing the brooding melodramatic act, pumped with anti-depressants to cope with imaginary dilemmas of torment. It's hard to make out his eyeliner beneath vintage square rimmed glasses, as his black-die greasy hair covers 3/4ths of his face at an angle. For the fourth time in twenty minutes he rants about his tragic depressing life, while hiding that he's cribbed up to the eyeballs living with his parents in a wealthy suburban lifestyle. If asked where he lives, you'll hear "The depths of living hell," while he scratches a canker sore with his black painted fingernails. Whining to no one in particular, he occasionally collapses onto his knees with puddles of self-loathing tears. It's a repeat performance Techno geek effortlessly ignores, and has me rolling in laughter.

Too depressed to bath, more mood swings than a PMS feminist, Emo spends his suicidal evenings crying and writing shitty ballads while strumming a lone string on his acoustic guitar. What a complete waste of oxygen. His conception probably took place backstage at a Wham! Concert during a chorus of *Wax on, Whack Off.*

If I had the time, I'd pick him up by his dyed hair, and drag him to the nearest beach and bury him up to the neck using a sledgehammer. Then I'd park an ex-lax chomping elephant above his dome.

-   -   -

Pondering my own day's schedule, I hold my throbbing head up by the chin, and find little chance of coherency. My brain hovers in the foggy 50% IQ range, as a 16 hour flight and binge drinking make me feel particularly vague. But if I can just perk up a bit, I'd be inclined to challenge my grandfather to a game of Dementia Trivia, except I can't remember how to play, and he died two decades ago, so for now I'll sit here looking brain dead with Godsmack blasting in my earplugs, and who doesn't love a meandering incoherent sentence, except if it includes a group encounter with Oprah and Perky Suzie. Giving up the feeble attempts at brilliant thought, Brett settles for some quality belching, while holding the newspaper high near my pink slits for eyes, whipping through the pages in search of full service strip clubs, happy hour parties, and escort ads.

After five minutes even the pictures prove too daunting, so I drop Moscow's finest propaganda rag. Feeling an unexpected rush from last night visuals, I instinctively lift my curious eyes. Peering through the Oakley's, it seems under the glass table the Lolita blondie is sitting legs spread a bit wide without panties.

My nostrils fantasize. The pussy sniff-o-meter is pinned. With her heavy lidded bedroom eyes locked on me, she's eating a foot-long frankfurter like it's a Barely Legal audition.

-   -   -

A freckled redhead waitress appears and takes my brunch order; she's a homely, stacked teen from the provinces, flauntingly proud of her 60 word English repertoire. Having been served nasty wrong meals here before, I point to the menu and order a verified safe meal - Western Omelet; the #17.

"What the hell…bring me a double Bloody Mary" handing her back the menu. While smirking at my blonde neighbor, I add "and a slice of her pussy."

The waitress leaves confused, and clomps off to the kitchen in cement sounding square clodhopper shoes, worn and faded from beating miles of sidewalk, and beating Vladimir over the head for yet another night of a loose interpretation of date rape. Some Uncles just never take a hint.

She brings another espresso and the Bloody Mary, and clunks away scratching her butt. Downing the espresso, the blood perks up in the veins, restoring color to my post-Vodka guzzling vampire skin tone.

Ahh, Moscow.

A city in a hurry.

The majesty 15th-17th century skyline of grandiose imperialist Czarist traditions – still remaining are some shades of the Baroque style, the Classical period with swirling arching spires, and vine covered churches and museums.

Decadent architecture. Magnificent monstrosities.

Pure Russia.

They're rapidly being erased by an obscene thirst for real estate profit. Bogus construction signs posted are merely disguised future demolitions of many historical buildings. They're being replaced with featureless glass and steel office towers, or larger than life hybrid Neo-Stalinist modern structures; simplistic facades with columns, topped by simulated medieval turrets or domes. McSkyscrapers and McCastles.

They're sprouting up from every corner. Disappointing changes indeed, but a few billionaires and their Rubles leave a lasting impression, particularly when their beefy thug wives are on the zoning board. A flip of the coin can decide what remains of the face of history. In this case, it's like tearing down the Eiffel Tower and the Statue of Liberty and planting high-rise Wal Marts.

Mega-bucks High-Rise construction beyond Arbat Street

Despite the obnoxious pounding jackhammers screaming above the rush hour traffic, the old déjà vu smile paints my face. So many insane Moscow memories, and yet so many more to come. Even sucking in the icy blue taxi exhaust is like the perfume of an old girlfriend, as it means Brett is once again living large and chilling in this monstrous Eastern Bloc sex capital…where every ten feet is a potential hook up. Girls. Sex. Everywhere.

-    -   -

As the hairs on the back of my neck rise, the unmistakable sweet, musky scent of femininity tickles my nose. Panning the area and seeing the table across is vacant, it's obvious it's now show time. A gaze down next to my chair finds shiny, black-laced knee-high S&M boots attached to some well-earned smooth athletic thighs.

And now on the main stage, Hot Dog Girl.

I slowly tilt my head back and ride them sexy wheels up with my eyes, savoring the crotch pit stop a bit too long. There's so much wet steam pouring out, I may need a snorkel to go down on her. Not that her healthy perky breasts pointing towards Stockholm and Tokyo at once are without merit. They were clearly imported from the highest stock in the Alps. When she laughs, her boobies slap together with a healthy declaration of *I'm available right now* femininity. But they were upstaged before the flirting even began.

No. It was definitely that mouth. Those juicy michelin lips were created for one thing, and she has every intention to suck the life right out of me, one drop at a time. Save me Oprah!

Completing the tour up her tight package, I find myself staring into intense blue eyes with long luxurious lashes, her scalp glistening through curly whitish-blonde tresses stretching down within inches from the crack of her ass. Hot Dog Girl taps a high heel impatiently, and announces her presence by running her index finger across my lips, returning it and sucking on the finger. It gets buried deep between wet pinkish lips so full, they'd send weaker men into a Careflight emergency copter. She leans forward with the healthy erect nipples of a teenager and teases in a sultry bedroom voice;

"Did u vant dat slice on da plate, or da face?"

Nice! Sexually aggressive. Full of vice. Plus a healthy command of English slut lingo.

"That depends if it's well-manicured and in season."

Inching her micro-miniskirt higher, the hem rides up till I can see the honey clearly.

Ahhhh. *Pure Russia.*

She gives a little girly girl giggle, loving me staring at her shaved pussy. She purrs;

"Virgin ripe und squeaky clean. Joo vant taste, babee?"

"Not right now, honey. Keep it warm for me."

At the exact wrong time, the stacked Plain Jane waitress arrives with my Western Omelet. She glances over at the exposed shaven appetizer, and asks me with a jealous stone face;

"Did joo vant dat for here or to go?"

"Both," I say, leaning forward and taking a long slow lick up her wet pussy lips. Does this café have great service of what?!

A shrill scream slices through the air, followed by a deep, nasally shrieking launched in my direction through gritted teeth.

"You disgusting pig!

"Who wants to see this?!!"

"Don't you have any sense of decency?"

I whip my head around towards the yelling, with snatch splooge flying from my tongue in slow-mo like chin blood from a Rocky punch. Brett lives for these moments. OMFG! It's the same gargantuan mega-beast and her miserable husband from my hotel lobby last night! The toxic whale has steam pouring out her ears like a runaway locomotive.

Pure fury.

How great is that!

She's perched on two seats like a giant beached sea turtle, leering at me with that throwing daggers look her husband has come to fear. He gets it at home when she's lying on her side on the couch and he's a tad slow bringing her the popcorn bowl to take a massive dump in.

Looking with pure love at that swollen pit bull face, I reply.

"Don't talk about yourself like that, Shamu. You may weigh a sloppy 345, but I bet when the lights are down, you don't look an ounce over 340 (rimshot!). When the waitress gave you the menu, did you reply "That'll do!"

She replies back with some nonsense, so I lovingly respnd.

"When you asked the hotel manager about the all-you-can-eat buffet, I bet they installed speed bumps. Let me guess, you use a mattress for a tampon?" (and other nice things).

The beaten down husband's eyes are frozen on the snapper, transfixed by the presence of something so Holy. He's bitten his lip, the blood trickling down and matting in his trimmed gray beard. Turning reluctantly towards his beefy wife, and again back to the coochie mirage, his drooping head buckles lower to half mast, bouncing off the chest with a sickly thud, shaking with a nervous tick back and forth.

"Don't get yourself down Pops. Ripe teen pussy is *sooo* overrated."

Sadly, our conversation was brief, as they fled in horror. When Shamu waddled by my table, the salt and pepper shakers, the ketchup and the drinks bounced and hopped an impromptu Latin Mambo across the slate, nearly plummeting off the edge. With the trained eye of a navy seals sniper, I note the sidewalk merely sustained hairline cracks, so the table won't crash through to the subway.

no fatties

Moments later in the street, a work crew straps her down on a flatbed like a grain silo. As the Peterbilt inches away, the tranny moans and smokes in disapproval at the excess tonnage.

-　-　-

Hot dog Lolita looks damn ecstatic having caused so much trouble. She winks at me with warm darting eyes seeking approval, and moves in for the kill. Leaning forward, she presses her budding perky puffies into me, and licks my cheek like a dog!

Wooffff !

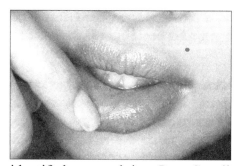

Picturing myself holding on a leash and she sits nude on all fours lapping at vodka in a doggie bowl, she hands me her cell digits written on a napkin. I'm momentarily stunned.

She's autographed it with a red lipstick kiss so gigantic; I could identify her mouth in a Porn Star lineup.

"Address han apartment number on back. Don vait too long."

Mmmmm. Another delicious *dyev* in distress. She earns a top listing for things that require further research. I wonder how long she lasts in the room till the vibrator comes out?

I save her cell under the name **THE MOUTH**. She gives me her best Cheshire Cat smile, turns, and throws in a final lift of the skirt, in case I didn't get a good enough whiff. I crack a smile, she smiles her crack; the whole exit is totally crackin'!

With a steely eyed determination, the Russian military babes march towards a battalion of defenseless Sybians.

10.
THE NAVY SEAL COOCHIE BANDIT

W hen in Moscow, late afternoon calls for witnessing Moscow's majestic architectural wonders in the historic tourist traps. Not the buildings, of course, I'm referring to hunting the city's other heart stopping sights parading around in high heels and a cloud of insatiable hormones.

Working the streets like a professional coochie hacker, Brett pursues a dangerous covert operation that should only be executed by an elite operative. Or, if you're a newbie in a hurry, you could always just wink and tape a $100 to your crotch. Trolling the streets for hot young gazelles, I'll be alternating personalities for each style girl, from the mysterious slippery stud to the wide-eyed, curious gringo with a camera, a smile, and raging hard-on.

My Targets?

Moscow is a massive cosmopolitan city. Every day babes full of Emerald City dreams arrive from some frozen hell hole province 1000 miles away, looking to experiment, indulge, explore, and conjure up a materialistic lifestyle out of thin air. Find a sexy teen *dyev* hiding her stuff in second-hand clothes with wandering eyes taking tourist photos or window-shopping, and it's like shooting fish in a barrel. For the fashionable foreigner, even many veteran female residents are easy prey, looking to hook up just for adventure.

The buffet of choices is diverse. Bored repressed trophy girlfriends with nympho genes, headstrong Lolitas from the Provinces with

pressing financial needs, to deeply introspective yet emotionally fragile girls with dead end day jobs.

The only way to see a foreign city is through a local's eyes, heart and soul - - - and what better way to do it than to relieve them of their panties in the process. It's a gallant quest, but at a cost of a few lunches and drinks, Brett is up to the challenge.

First stop is the number one tourist attraction, the most recognizable building of Moscow, located just outside the Kremlin in the Red Square. The infamous **St. Basil's Cathedral** commissioned and built by Ivan the Terrible in the 1555, known for its stunning array of swirling colored onion dome-topped towers. Inside these dimly lit chapels are a fascinating series of maze-like hallways, with walls covered in floral designs painted in stunning pastel colors.

The gigantic Red Square courtyard is the central point for tourists and landmarks. It's also the meeting point for mingling locals, wedding parties taking photos, as well as endless wandering tourists.
Great place to hook up.

On the eastern side of the Red Square opposite the St. Basil's Cathedral is Gum Dept. Store; one of the largest and most expensive shopping venues in the world, with a front façade of 265 yards. It's a millionaire wife's fantasy shopping camp, home to hundreds of obscenely priced high dollar designer boutiques. Only the elite can afford to shop here. It creates a perfect scenario to meet a daydreaming window shopper, or spontaneous college student. Buy her a morning cappuccino and discuss the architecture and arts, and then spend the afternoon with her ankles pinned behind her ears while she screams like a wild banshee. Like clockwork.

Built 1893, the Gigantic GUM Department Store in the Red Square

Back home, flirting with hotties and models will get you the finger, laughed at in the face, and treated like you have the plague. In everyday life in Moscow, far more gorgeous women constantly eye you up and down like sexual predators. Even if they're not giving you signals, if you approach them with simple conversation, almost all will stop and say hello. In just a few short hours there are endless opportunities to collect a dozen numbers and plot your dating and sex schedule.

Technique? If you can call it that, I stroll around smiling and ask the girls simple stuff; *Vi gavaritie pa Engliiski?* - do you speak English?"

I ask their name, ask what city they're from, ask where some landmark is, we take tourist photos, and pretty soon we're pounding shots, sucking face, I'm tugging on her thong, and it's either straight to the hotel or I'm leaving with a lipstick cheek and her digits.

One date and Brett the Beast is banging these upper tier babes and treating them like dirt, and they look at me with love struck eyes. Russian girls are like no other women you will experience. No matter how classy and sophisticated they look, they live for vices and adventure, and are always sexual freaks in the sack. A few swigs of vodka will dispel any conservative Eastern women view you have, as their pussies immediately catch fire, resulting in you being defenseless and sexually assaulted. You learn pretty quickly the girls love a guy who is aggressive and direct, and they like it rough.

There is a serious caste system amongst women here. In a city with gorgeous women on every street corner, where pay for play is the rule of the land, you can accelerate your babe hunting to outlandish opportunities when you approach the second tier girls.

Women here are considered cougars and on their last legs by their mid twenties! *Attention MILF shoppers*. In Moscow, girls from age 25 to 29 are considered the crusty over the hill crop. Past their prime

and no longer able to compete, they are usually single moms who Boris dumped for a ripe younger squeezebox.

In the early mornings, if you cruise the Metro a few stops away out of town, you'll find these over the hill hotties buying groceries, babysitting someone's kids, or dropping their own kids off to school. It's very, very easy to meet scorching hot single moms and have an afternoon date and eventual hookup, and/or get a referral date from them.

What about the dyev Grannies…the 30-36 year old dinosaurs or heaven forbid those 40 year old senior citizens? Be forewarned. It will take some time to weed out the cattle. Russian women tend to explode at the waist around thirty; it goes from shooting fish in a barrel to harpooning at Sea World. However, if this is your target market and you're patient, you'll find some prime targets who will beg for your attention, you disgusting fossil fucker!

Stunning intricate ceiling of the Christ the Savior Cathedral

- - -

The day is getting long in a hurry. It's been a busy afternoon of sightseeing and daytime hookups, resulting in a pocket full of numbers I'll never call. Working my way back to the hotel, a mild breeze carrying sexy perfume tickles my nose with temptation. I park with a tray of cocktails and set up my voyeur shop. There's nothing like relaxing with an umbrella drink in an outdoor cafe in Moscow, nestled in your sniper nest watching the endless parade of the most beautiful white women in the world strolling by every two seconds.

I end up getting sidetracked and bloody smashed in a late afternoon pub crawl, packed to the gills with long legs and eye candy for miles. Today's tour started in cafes packed with rich spoiled *Blondnikas* sponsored by fat cats with so much excess cash, the girls may as well have been attached to a gold leash. Judging by their twitching noses, it's safe to say a nearby table of four hotts could actually be the 2nd largest importer of Colombian goods for the last few years.

As the hours progressed into the early evening, a steady procession of cute to stunning *babealushkas* flow into the cafés, in search of their favorite companions; icy vodka, and today's fuck buddy. My pace of liquor accelerates in tandem with lecherous flirting, in broken Russian that vaguely resembles a conversation. Soon I have a buffet of perky *dyevs* with wandering hands tugging on my bar tab and butt and crotch, competing for the dirty deed. I keep trying to leave, but the Johnson and liver remain persistent, particularly concerning a certain jailbait Lolita playing video solitaire, smacking her bubblegum and twirling her hair in between blowjob offers. Sitting perched on a barstool in a schoolgirl outfit hiked up, after the third pink thong cameltoe shot my head nearly exploded into candy.

In the midst of doing shots and sucking face with Katerina and the rack twins, Ivanka, and Dasha(?)-Masha(?), a waitress with sky high peroxide blonde hair comes out of the kitchen to deliver a B-Day cake to a nearby table. Unknown to her, her thick hairspray bouffant gets too close to one of the candles, so she arrives all perky at the table singing Happy Birthday with flames shooting out of hair like an exploding rocket.

A manager observes the spectacle and does a Ray Lewis end around blitz and tackles her with a table cloth over her head, which launches the cake airborne across the table, smack into the face of the birthday girl with a gigantic gassppllatt. Birthday girl hops up and does a Holyfield roundhouse into the manager's jaw, which knocks him out cold. He lands face first on the floor next to the waitress, who lies smoldering in a pile like a string of Chinatown firecrackers screaming *Vot da Fuck*!

Out of the kindness of my heart, I was tempted to whip it out and golden shower the bitch to quiet the embers. But being a stranger to Russian customs, and seeing as everyone in the room is distracted, in a panic I open Ivanka's blouse and slobber all over her nipples, while one hand slides under Katerina's skirt and strokes her cameltoe for a dipstick taste test. Despite my icy calm and permanent intravenous vodka drip, if it weren't for a prior engagement this evening, it would have escalated into a marathon all-you-can-eat orgy with some fine young party sluts.

Sorry Katerina. Sorry Ivanka. Sorry Whatever.

11.

GANGSTER STYLING IN THE ULTIMATE PARTY CRIB

This afternoon is the business meeting with Viktor's mentor, who wants to invest with us. Dmitry is an extremely wealthy shrewd businessman, who is partially legit, as well as a feared, ruthless gangster. In Moscow the two careers go hand in hand. Thug beezinessman are the side of the law you want to be on in Russia, as they are far more trustworthy. There's no need to have to grease palms every level and jump through regulatory hoops. These meetings are usually a quick meet and greet that builds over a few days before a decision is made. In Japan, this is done over a round of golf. In Moscow you feel each other out during a few vodka laden meetings, followed by blowing the roof off in nights of wretched excess and sleaze in VIP strip clubs and P4P honey holes. I've done my research on the client and vice versa, so this is really a formality.

There are two types of wealth: new money, and quiet money. New money is all flash and image. Every move draws attention to it. It's all designer labels, the right expensive toys, and varies from Bond coolness to nauseating insecure ego.

Then there is *quiet money*.

Being rich for many years, one finds a veil of secrecy is more valuable and powerful. Quiet money bends rules. It stays below the radar. It helps hide you from the bad guys looking to carve out a slice of your pie for themselves. It also helps you hide from the really bad guys trying to empty your entire pocket, like predatory women, parasite attorneys, and the IRS. More importantly, quiet money is mysterious and attracts more women. Girls have superhuman money detection genes; they can smell it a mile away, and size you up like you're a walking UPC code.

Viktor arrives like clockwork exactly at 5:47pm. His gorgeous piano-black Aston Martin weaves like a demon away from Moscow's central zone through side streets that with each turn become more desolate and barren. Crossing over the Moskva River, we travel ten minutes into the outskirts of the provinces, circling down a series of dirt roads. We steer into a decaying old warehouse district, devoid of any life. A black Ducatti motorcycle is idling facing us; the headlights flash twice, and Viktor flashes his lights back, turns right and parks. The landscape looks like the 19th century Wild Wild West. No signs of Clint Eastwood anywhere. No signs of any activity.

No businesses. No people. Nothing.

This is quiet money.

- - -

W e stroll through a deserted maze of buildings, kicking our way through a distressed landscape of propane canisters, crushed beef stew cans, deflated soccer balls, and aged Khrushchev propaganda leaflets. After we negotiate an inner corridor of twists and turns, a huddle of massive flathead mutants appear in knee length leather coats, chain-smoking fiercely outside a rusted black door. They have massive round chests, scarred square jaws below discolored foreheads housing deep set hollowed eyes.

Retiring from the Bolshoi Ballet, Ivan aims for Dancing with the Stars.

Big scary men.
Armed and terminally pissed.

"Brett, Dmitry is connected thug und a pig, but he smartest beez-nis-man I've ever met. Prophetic street smarts. Da heat he packs is damage control. He no like surprises" he says, brushing dirt from the right shoulder of his black leather bomber jacket, and removing his shades and placing them in an inner flap pocket.

"Shoot first, ask questions later."
Viktor flashes the no worries sign to me.

The client's bodyguards have catcher's mitt sized hands; each is tilting back liters of straight vodka like Colorado spring water, from faded bottles without labels. Their faces devoid of emotion, with a frozen glare of coldness. They look like they haven't blinked in years. Disgusted grunts announce a glaring lack of violence, while a few check their weapons' sights and safety.

"Door please." The closest guy cranks it open, while his fellow liquored up thugs whistle and catcall down the street at two fifteen year old schoolgirls strutting by, who casually flip them off, disappearing into a picturesque diesel cloud sunset. The Ducatti cycle goes whipping past doing a 40mph wheelie, kicking up black soot and gravel and glass into the girls' legs. They scream like they're running from Freddie Krueger, breaking out into a futile sprint to try and avoid getting sprayed. The bodyguards howl in laughter and tilt back their bottles.

-    -   -

The massive empty warehouse is dimly lit by stray bulbs swinging at the end of a frayed cord like a pendulum, creaking in defiance. The corner of the first room is populated with a weathered hanging punching bag, and a dartboard covered with throwing knives and Chinese stars. At our feet, the cement is littered with gun shells, German Sports car mags, junk food wrappers, vermin scrambling in mold, and a three-foot monument of empty Vodka bottles. It's like a home for alcoholic martial arts squatters.

"Vladimir...you sure da boss didn't say
go pick me up some Whores?"

Nearly choking on decade old cement dust, we make our way quickly through vacant cavernous areas, the clomping of our shoes echoing two and three times off the warehouse walls. As the air becomes wet and dank smelling, we disappear down an extended narrow tunnel of peeling drywall and drooping ceiling tiles in near darkness, walking through numerous doors like the Get Smart intro. The end appears unexpectedly, revealing a guarded elevator. Viktor nods to the expressionless flathead, an imposing monster with an impossible skull that protrudes out three inches at the forehead.

We cruise up the elevator two stories. It opens into a drawing area that leads presumably to the investor's office. No receptionist, no secretary. No look at me fanfare. It's just your typical office door blocked by a ripped, focused ex-SpetsNaz (Special Forces) bodyguard who may be the largest human being I've ever seen. About 6'10" and yet a chiseled 375 pounds...even his hair has muscles. He has a Tommy gun crooked in his right arm, and a shoulder strapped Kalashnikov AK-47. An expressionless face with steely blue eyes surrounding a pockmarked face autographed with a five-inch purple-ridged knife scar on his right cheek. The boss can't completely shut out the public, but he certainly doesn't like being bothered.

The brickhead nods and using a hand like a shovel, opens the vault-like door. The door slams behind with an echoing click that makes me wince.

- - -

Facing the wall, a high back leather chair conceals the investor. He's sitting behind a huge redwood conference desk, waving his arms madly while barking orders into a phone. He glances around at us and gives a circular finger motion, spinning back away from us in his chair, continuing his conversation.

"He vants us to take-a da grand tour. Brett, vait till joo see deez."

What can I say? After strolling through an abandoned cement warehouse, I didn't have high expectations. The office décor screams of thick irony. The guy comes up big. He is a fucking whale. His office is a cross between a Vegas Penthouse suite and Tony Montana's bedroom in Scarface.

An 8000 sq. ft L-shaped pad, it has cathedral ceilings with huge floor to ceiling marble Corinthian columns connecting ornate archways with mosaic carved designs. The space is sectioned into three areas; a game room, lounging area, and mahogany paneled conference hall. Under the beveled marble ceilings against one wall are a line of intricate marble statues of erotic nude women on stands, carved glass tables and burl veneer furniture resting on burgundy carpeting with gold trim. Everything is classy with a cornucopia of sexual overtones and exquisite touches of trim dripping with gold. Not to mention every time I blink a different naked chick in heels is strolling through the room winking at us.

Ostentatious. Gluttonous. In your face Rich.

The Gangster Pimp Daddy Entertainment Room

"Brett. Dmitry's entertainment room eez da sheet. Joove got leather recliners and side sofas facing an enormous state of dee art wall projection screen. Dere's 61" Sony plasmas on each side for multiple displays of sports or porn when da strippers are here. Left eez a huge fireplace with intricate gold trim designs reaching all da vaay up to a 21 foot ceiling. Da right corner eez an elevated circular stage vith a gold stripper pole."

We both laugh and share a cynical wink.

The Johnson starts lecturing me:

"First you get the money, then with the money you get the power. When you get the power, THEN you get the women."

Clearly the boss and I share the same priorities; he just has a lot more zeros and commas. The right wall is home to vintage gun racks with a few trophy heads mounted; a Lion, a Bear, a Rosie O'Donnell head, all the scary beasts of the jungle.

"For sound, joove got rows of ceiling flush mounted Bose speakers, coupled with Vandersteen wall, floor and center speakers. Top notch stuff."

Familiar with the setup, I pan the room and locate the missing ingredient; a set of corner Klipsch sub-woofer speakers PA sized.

"Da right corner is party central for da chicks. A six person black marble Jacuzzi, dual sinks trimmed with da baroque gold leaf, with wall and ceiling mirrors, and stocked liquor cabinets."

Next to the tub I can't help but notice is a pile of lace see-through panties and rabbit dildos.

We walk to the other side of the room. The game room area has several gigantic circular crushed velvet couches resting on a massive bear skin rug. Under crystal chandeliers, there's an 8 ft. pool table with gold trim, vintage video games and pinball machines and a dart board. Beneath a swan-neck light curling out, a large swath of the wall is decorated with a large 6' X 4' lurid Vargas-like painting of a greased up naked girl on all fours wearing a dog collar; her leash is held by an Amazon Goddess in a cat woman mask wearing nothing but thigh high boots and a dirty grin.

She's holding a whip and looks pissed. A nice touch.

The Johnson pans the room and highly approves; *"greed is good. Greed is right. Greed works."*

The complete Gangster Pimp Daddy crib.

-   -   -

T he investor spins around in his high back leather chair and slams his phone down, unwrapping a Cuban cigar while muttering to himself. He's parked behind a gigantic ballroom sized cherry redwood desk fit for a King, covered with thirty odd stacks of 1000 and 5000 ruble banknotes eighteen inches high, surrounding a Magnum 44. A squat, scruffy man as wide as he is tall spins and stands up, chomping the unlit cigar and grinning ear to ear. He reeks of liquor, smoke and stripper skank cologne. Up to the gills in money living large, his energy is contagious.

"Viktor, joo crazy young fool. Come here and show Dmitry some respect, before I piss all over jour leg!"

With Viktor's help, I checked out Dmitry's dossier and come to a very familiar resume for oligarch Moscow wealth. Ivy League MBA. Mafia seed money turned venture capitalist turned risk management expert. When Yeltsin "privatized" – plundered the state assets during the 1991 Soviet Collapse, Dmitry had the brains, balls and snake oil connections to pick off a few pieces of his own.

Shortly thereafter, this investment provided him with the seed capital to his first traceable fortune; buying up bargain basement shares of oil and mining stocks. (Oil was in the teens then). He liquidated the bulk of his holdings as the Asian Contagion market debacle started.

In the late '90s when the Soviet empire disintegrated and the Russian ruble crashed, he was perfectly positioned for his next wave of wealth. After the recovery started to take hold, and re-entered his oil positions, and now is one of the countless men you've never heard of, who happen to have several hundred million dollars. He's Fat Cat rich by a geo-historical accident coupled with a shrewd business sense. Of course that may be pennies compared to his unknown ventures. The only place you'll see more insane wealth taken for granted is Dubai.

- - -

Standing before Dmitry is like walking into a time machine and meeting a 1920's Russian Al Capone. The scene is intimidating. The man is an armed gangster, a gluttonous pig, offensive, drunk, and devoid of one ounce of class. I like him immediately. In short time, I'll find him to be a contagious rouge full of piss and vinegar and dirty caveman jokes; enough to offend almost anyone.

"Brett, I'm so sorry about da mess. I'm afraid I have habit of running too many cash beez-niss-ez. Bwwahhahhahahh," in a belly wobbling Jabba the Hut chuckle. Get that. He apologized for having more than half a million dollars in cash on his table. Shifting his stance, he checks the safety and places a polished silver Smith and Wesson 50 caliber handgun on the table before shaking hands with a rough, sweaty vice grip.

"Brett Tate, it's a pleasure. Nice pad. Were you a pimp in your past life, or current?"

"Eetz disgusting isn't it! Da! I love it. In life, it not so important to win or lose, just as long as you piss somebody off! Dat's bullshit of course. I always win, and I always piss somebody off," Bwahaahaahaa.

Dmitry walks to the wall behind his desk and swings open a large Al Capone painting, like there's a safe behind it. Instead, there's a beautiful teak wood bordered see-thru crystal glass refrigerator, mounted flush into the wall. He pulls out several different liters of icy cold vodka and three 3 inch tall shot glasses. You drink Vodka by the shot in Russia. No pansy pseudo-candy liquor. Russians don't dilute the purity. He has the high quality stuff you'll rarely find in clubs back home.

Snow Queen, Kaufmann, Imperia and Diva Premium Vodka. We choose Kauffman, made with water extracted from a glacial lake.

Dmitry pours the first round. Man does the good stuff go down smooth. Normal high-end US vodka is distilled four times; this stuff is processed some eight to twelve times. Viktor puts the big screen on in the background. The clarity of picture is stunning, easily the best I've ever seen, and it's a projection screen no less. I must say, Oprah has never looked so good. You could cut the emotional sensitivity with a knife. There wasn't a dry eye in the room.

"Brett, Capone was visionary. One of sharpest US beeziness minds in 20th century. The man would feel at home in Moscow today, although he might not be corrupt enough."

His comments are a mouthful. Dmitry is sarcastic, and speaks the cold truth. Like so many Oligarchs, his wealth came about like Capone's prohibition empire; a short window exploited when a snoozing government made an irreversible mistake and succumbed to a bandit capitalism epoch.

"Nobody knows directions to office, Brett," Viktor adds with squinting eyes and a smirk. "Joo must be driven to get in. Dmitry sent the limo and blindfolded all da interior design installers each day

coming and going, so dey no can spread the word or come back and steal their stuff back."

"Fuck them greedy bastards. They triple bill me for everything!" Dmitry says, with eyes flaring and spittle building on his lips. "They do nice work,

though, the thieves. Some guys spend all night looking for the best party. I bring the party here. Mine are usually better."

"Brett, come here. Let me show you something."

He walks us behind a series of hanging curtains to an entrance. After negotiating three separate locks, he opens the thick door. It's hiding a palatial fat cat crib so over the top it has to be seen to be believed. It's a 6000 sq. foot studio L-shaped bedroom.

The Pimp Daddy's Crib – Jacuzzi, kitchen and maid quarters down the hall

A vast open air space with yet another monstrous entertainment center on a wall, and a massive elevated bed with an enormous headboard. In the foyer, a delicious hottie is nestled in front of a glossy ebony Steinway. She's playing a stirring Abba ballad from their hardcore protest years. Butchering it with an uncanny sense of hopelessness, she eventually gives up and segues into the old dependable; a horrid interpretation of chop sticks. I get down on my knees and bow, praising her god-given ivory skills, while aching to get down into the sprinter starter blocks and charge forward, pushing in her tight stool.

The furniture in the bedroom is immaculate, belonging in the castle of Louis XV. Far left corner of the room is a waiting area, with plush couches and oversize wall paintings of naked Renaissance women. The floor is covered with fine handmade Persian rugs. Up above, glittering gold chandeliers and natural light shining through stained glass ceiling windows carved out of the white marble ceiling. Overlooking the fireplace, the ceiling has artwork painted in the style of the Sistine Chapel, highlighted by subtle track lighting. Around the L corner of the room, there's a palatial bathroom, with a Pearl White 6-person Jacuzzi, glass showers and walk-in closet. We peek in the closet. Viktor walks to the end and brushes aside a row of lingerie and schoolgirl, nurse, cop, and maid outfits, and there's a hidden elevator. Nice.

"Dees is just his offeez and bachelor pad" Viktor explains, while Dmitry disappears through swinging French doors to take a whiz, while blowing his nose violently and ripping a gigantic fart.

"Dmitry has many rental properties and a few penthouse condos off Tverskaya for fun, and for appearances da out of town castle dat he rarely visits."

- - -

We leave the crib, and head back into the lounge area and shoot a game of pool, tossing back half a dozen shots and a few beers each while talking shop. (It's in my best financial interests not to explain business details. Let's just say I buy things, sell things, and keep most of it for myself. All of us are middlemen.) We lay out the basic financial terms, liabilities and profit structure in short notice. Frankly, Dmitry seems bored and embarrassed to be having the discussion. When Viktor leaves for the bathroom in the bedroom, Dmitry gives me the come here index finger and leans in close, speaking quietly.

"Brett, joo don't know Viktor's childhood, do you?"

"We hold only surface personal discussions. If one of us wants to divulge details, it's up to him."

"Dat's vott I thought. Viktor eez a tough kid. His parents were murdered when he was seven. He settled in as a young boy with a pack of steely-eyed driven mentors. Some of us are even partially legit. (Bwwwahhaahhaa). He vaas fortunate to receive an education in da trenches, surrounded by influential people vith diverse personalities. He listened and learned, and engaged in select pieces of identity theft, until he found his own. He's a good kid. Smart kid."

I lean back and pour us two shots. We down them in silence.

"In Moscow, Joo don't give jour kids money. Joo make dem learn the system. Learn how to make money. Use it. Respect it. Da tools are more important than the jewels." He takes a long hit from his Cohiba and downs the rest of his beer.

"Joo have done good things for Viktor, taken him under joo wing, and like myself helped make him wealthy and sharp.

Dat's why joo are here. Dat's why I'm extending a credit line for a piece…out of appreciation. Not a verd to him about deez, okay?"

A quick clink of drinks and a nod.

"Nostrovia. Viktor is like my kid brother. He deserves an edge. Dmitry, I'm sure we'll do business a long time, although for a minute there I thought you were going to start singing We are the World."

"Brett, eetz shots time, my good man" pointing a finger gun at me.

"Agreed!" chimes Viktor as he walks into the room.

"Viktor, a change of pace" says Dmitry. Bring us a round of Diva Premium shots….you'll like deez stuff, Brett. Eetz da good stuff. "

-   -   -

An interesting exchange. In my first meet with Dmitry, I can see a lot of him in Viktor. I have a feeling he practically raised Viktor as his own blood. Viktor returns with the shots, which are icy cold and fantastic.

"So what's the story about Mr. Zero at your front door?"

Viktor's eye bulge, head shaking a no while staring at me with concern. Dmitry catches this, nods his head side to side and waves a relaxed dismissing hand to Viktor.

"Brett. There are many things I cannot tell you about me," gazing at me with coal black eyes…piercing eye contact, shifty and full of intensity. This will be the only moment I witness his fire the whole trip. The rest of the time his eyes twinkle with laughter.

Dmitry leans back and takes a long draw on his Cohiba exhaling a swirling bulls-eye cloud; intently watching its path towards the ceiling like an air traffic controller. He leans forward and pours us each a shot of Diva Premium, and then quietly examines the label like it's a long lost friend. With a heavy sigh, he replaces the bottle on the table. We chug and sit for a few moments in silence. Mmm. Exquisite vodka. I'm certainly not going to push the topic any further.

He leans forward, mildly whispering in a football huddle.

"Mr. Zero as you call him….I like dat….Mr. Zero is da closer when beeg beeziness situations go wrong. Competitive turf wars. Dat kind of stuff. He has a whole team dat *even I* don't know about. Don't vant to know actually" leaning back with out-of-focus eyes scanning the mosaic ceiling tile.

"I'd think those days are numbered. Putin appears to be an even bigger thorn in Moscow capitalism after the state seized Yukos."

"Da!" Dmitry says bouncing forward in his seat, his eyes lit up. This is definitely a hot button issue for him.

"The KGB is back in beeziness running the government, seizing assets for eetz piggybank, suppressing dissent in da papers, all dat. Centralized control is da death knell for da free markets. Joo know dat, eetz been killing western capitalism for 20 years."

"So the turf wars have diverted into an asset protection race."

"Exactly, Brett. No more transparency. Most of da beeg money has left dee country and operates through shell companies and offshore trusts. Carefully I might add. Moscow's Wild West is mostly reduced to da club scene now, compared to your first trips here. Joo watch Brett. If oil crashes our exports will diminish, and down goes Moscow. Eetz a third of our national revenue, 65% of our exports. Da Great Bear is growling, but teetering on eetz knees at da same time."

Dmitry pours another round of shots, bouncing back up in the couch into the football huddle with a grin and wink.

"Mr. Zero's new passion is being da first responder to problems. An odd transition from da lethal closer." He stands and takes a shot at our forgotten pool game. We each take a shot and then Dmitry signals to sit. I pour more shots in silence and nod at him to continue.

"A month ago, dere was an incident with deez smart ass little bald attorney from Germany. He was several months late with a large final payment on a deal, and not returning calls. Mr. Zero pays him a visit. Meets him unexpectedly at his front door.

Dmitry leans back and draws deep on the Cuban cigar, savoring it before blowing a circular plume....followed by vodka shots....followed by a long weighty silence.

"Mr. Zero eez berry disciplined, a military trained professional. Ex-Spatnez (Special Forces) of course. He introduces himself with a beeziness card, berry calmly explains he's a private detective hired to collect my money. He opens his jacket and shows his Kalashnikov, and points to his car.

"Joo see dat Mercedes in da street? Dat's mine. Everywhere joo go, joo will see dat car. Most times I never bother people. Other times, I get impatient. I lose control. Eetz a military problem. Joo don't vant me to lose control around joo."

"In one week joo will pay Dmitry in full. Until then, every place joo go, every second of da day, I will be watching joo. My friends will be watching joo family. Good day."

"How long?" I ask.

"Two days tops is dee average for payment. The dumb ones end up wishing Mr. Zero used his gun. His hands and kicks are far more lethal. He takes his time ripping them to pieces too, a real sweetheart. Bwahhhahhhahhhh." Cigar puff, swirling cloud, pours vodka shot....long pause.

I lay out a few more preferred strokes for our proposed business. From my end I'm golden, as the first few deals Dmitry's piece will come out of Viktor's side. My risk is zilch, but the increased credit line can come in handy. After a few deals under the belt we'll adjust the terms. Dmitry gets bored of the conversation rather quickly.

"Enough business. Look, I trust Viktor and take his word. If anything goes wrong, I'll just cut off his deek. Now. Joo guys hungry? Let's get the hell out of here. I'm so hungry I could eat a fat American beetch." (chortlesnort, guffaw)

"Can't say I've ever been that hungry, Dmitry," I counter.

"Neither can I! Come. My driver's out back."

He speed dials a cell number.

"We leave in five minutes."

He places "the mess" on his desk into a safe, and off we go with Mr. Zero down the elevator and through a maze of doors until we reach a thick steel door. Dmitry knocks and yells his name. An armed gorilla opens the door. We walk through another series of corridors, until we reach another thick door.

"It pays to be paranoid, Brett," Dmitry says as he again knocks and yells, and out we go through a 6-inch thick vault-like door.

Out back is a circular courtyard, walled off with high fence topped with thick crisscrossing coiled barbwire. Guards and guns populate the asphalt in a flurry of activity. Pulling up to us and stopping is a black Mercedes stretch limo, with pitch-black tinted bulletproof windows. Idling angrily nearby is a British Racing green Murcielago, fresh from a mirror-like coat of wax. Nice.

Mr. Zero separates from us and walks over to an idling Land Rover, with three other armed goons already inside. A second Land Rover waits at the point near the gate, positioned to leave first. Turning around, the contrast between the warehouse building and Dmitry's crib inside couldn't be starker. A burly gruff guard appears near the rear door of the limo, smelling like a lineman's greasy armpit during an August practice. He opens the door for me. I lean forward, and Dmitry shoves me in and slams the door.

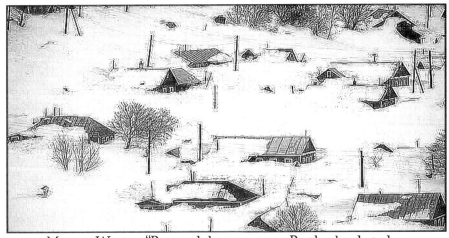

Moscow Winter: "Rise and shine campers. Partly cloudy today with a chance of flurries... a high of ~ 40 degrees."

12.
BISEXUAL ORGY IN A MCDONALDS DRIVE-THRU

Surprises are best when you least expect them. Dmitry shoved me into the limo, and inside it there are four smoking hot butt naked nymphs. They're wearing nothing but high heels, sprawled out on a circular couch, each holding and drinking a bottle of Sovyetskaya champagne.

Fleshy things of youth and eternal lust.

As substantial as any Russian mail order bride legend ever conceived. Cruel and unusual punishment. Dmitry opens the door howling in laughter like a boy who's just seen his first nipple.

Viktor and the big man hop in all grins and belches, as we whip a 360 and get set to leave the parking lot with the battalion of goons riding in Land Rovers in front and behind us. The girls go bouncing across the couches on top of each other, cackling like the tight little teenagers they are. It's hard to tell which one is sexiest. Or horniest. Or more drunk. Or legal.

"Brett. Velcome to my Church!"

- - -

The girls give Dmitry a nude group hug. Pimp daddy opens a fridge and removes two vodka bottles and pours shots, while chomping on his unlit cigar with slobber pouring out the side of his mouth.

"I'm in the mood for something sloppy and greasy….not you Olga! I vant Burgers und fries; something to make Brett feel right at home…"

"Strippers make me feel right at home."

"What, dees girls? They're just appetizers before we get some prime beef tonight. Joo been to Nightflight Brett?"

"I've dropped my son's college education there."

"You got kids?" asks Dmitry while cupping an impressive rack in one hand, an ass cheek in the other.

"None that I'd admit too," I confessed, focusing my sights on the pink taco buffet spread out before me.

"I figured that. Relax Brett. Joo know, most Americans think Russians are just a bunch of dirty fat bandits, raping and pillaging westerners. It's not true. Some of us are not fat."

-   -   -

A few miles from the palatial penthouse suite we pull into a drive thru McDonald's, off all places. During the ride, Dmitry jots down everyone's order on paper, while the girls put on a sexy little show lip-synching to the Pussy Cat Dolls blaring on the speakers. By the second chorus they forget all about the song and start sucking on each other's nipples to compare whose are longest. As we cruise into the McD's driveway, Dmitry gives the handwritten order to the hottest girl, while opening the rear moonroof.

"Jour turn to order Veronika," he says, while elbowing me hard in the side.

Coming to a halt at the squawking drive-through box, Veronika stands up butt naked through the moonroof. Dmitry winks at me, sliding off the half moon sofa seat onto his knees underneath her. His face is planted between her thighs, with a frozen frat brother's grin.

Picture this scene. The instant Veronika starts ordering, Dmitry cups her ass and starts licking her pussy. The other Lolitas burst out into contagious giggles, grabbing his fat ass and teasing him to lick faster.

"I vant three Bigga Mac, seven of da French uh fries and unnnhhh ooo ...oooOOOHOHHHH!" Veronika squeals. It turns out that little Veronika is a moaner. Dmitry backs off for a second. Huffing and puffing, she wipes the sexual perspiration off her forehead and regains her best McDonald's pussy-licked composure. The second she  starts ordering again, Dmitry dives in slobbering and going down on her like a convicted pedophile on a weekend prison furlough. The man sure knows how to impress a potential client.

"I like-a-da two chocolate ice cream, three chicken sandviches, six-a-da cokes and oooohhH..aaaAAAHHHH!!" Veronika squeaks out nearing the edge. Dmitry keeps lapping away like there's a licking time limit.

"Dmitry, less passion, more aggression!" I yell out, getting into the whole performance. Viktor nods like a condescending grandfather.

Across from me, Ms. Teen Siberia facing me defines raw sex appeal. Pure smut. Teasing me with heavy-lidded green bedroom eyes, she parts her long, caramel thighs spread eagle. Her flat tummy leads to a neatly trimmed pussy with pink, pouty lips slightly open and wet with moisture. Her eyes squint as she starts fingering herself. Talking dirty in Russian to me, with her other hand she lifts an empty champagne bottle and does a slow deep throat with it. Then she lowers it and parks the tip inside her steaming pink garage. Ouch. As she slowly pumps it, glistening drops of coochie juice gently cascade down her creamy thighs. *Bozhe moi.*

A view of the Gods.

Turning purple, I slap my own face and remember to breathe. She's my density. I fall in love. Wait till Mom meets her!

"Brett! Joo like extra sauce on your pink taco, Da?" Viktor chimes in enjoying my view, while bending the nearest girl over and spanking her ass.

His girl is on all fours giving me a nice rear vertical smile view. You go girl. She's a gorgeous little teenie, one exquisite piece of tight flesh from her neck down to her pink toenails on her perfect little tan feet. She crawls over to the horny babe facing me, removes the bottle, and starts licking her upper thighs; excruciatingly long licks up and down her legs until she tongues her labia lips gently. Moans fill the air. Viewing this gourmet spread laid out in front of me, I must say McDonald's has really gone all out in Moscow.

The fourth nymphet is lying across my lap on her side watching the oral show, while fingering herself. A smooth firm body, with perky  erect boobies that I eagerly play with, while raising my bottle in a silent toast. Her legs start trembling from a mini-orgasm, her naked little body twitches and presses back against mine. She pulls two fingers out of her gushing bald snatch to her mouth and sucks the juices from them.

Can't anybody wait for the fries and burgers around here?

The Johnson slams against the fabric of my trousers while I shift restlessly on the seat. Her skin is steaming warm. When I squint, her swollen meat wallet actually looks like a Big Mac. She lowers her head and starts licking both sides of my zipper, while squeezing my hard-on with her fingers. The limo is now filled with the unmistakable sweet smell of fresh young snatch. I take a deep whiff and smile, eyes bouncing from one girl to the next in feverish lust.

"I almost forgot. Viktor! Hand me Brett's gift!"

Viktor slides open a side compartment and hands a box to Dmitry. Dmitry opens it and holds up a gigantic blanket.

"Brett. Joo gonna love deez. Eetz vith great privilege I present joo vith jour Russian Rite of Passage."

I have to say, it's one of the funniest and most creative things I've ever seen in my life. On the bottom of the blanket in big letters it says King Brett, and above it is a huge coat of arms diagram of a King sitting in his throne, with a girl on her knees giving him a blowjob. It rocks! Wait till customs sees it!

"Eetz jour very own Royal Moscovian blowjob blanket. Eet should come in handy any minute now."

"Words cannot express my level of gratitude, Dmitry. It's a rare pleasure to do business with someone as magnificently twisted as yours truly." Shaking his hand, while with the other hand I clink Viktor and his tall shot glasses and raise mine for toast…

"Gentleman. May we live to see fifty."

"TO FIFTY!" goes around the limo.

"Don't think joo dat special Brett" Viktor chimes in, doing a fake pick of his nose with his middle finger. He reaches into the same sliding compartment and pulls out another blanket and flashes me his

King Viktor coat of arms. His has two girls on their knees. One upped by a younger man. You'll pay for that, ya dirty rotten bastard. He grabs one of the girls and lines her up between his legs on her knees. She wraps the blanket around herself and holds it high while Viktor shuffles a bit in his seat. His pants appear at his ankles. Hmmm. I like the system.

"I like-a-da von strawberry milk shake ooohhhH aaaAAAHHHH!!" Veronika screams and squeals, as Dmitry is devouring his main course. I grab my spinner and put her on her knees and do the same blanket thing. It's quite a view. All you see are the lower half of the blankets going up and down, and two idiots' heads hovering above them with stupid cartoon grins. To complete the view, across from me Champagne girl has resumed her lusty visual, and is giving me an awesome show. Legs spread facing me, she grabs her date, the champagne bottle, and guides it slowly in and out, while pinching her nipples and moaning. Nice.

Dmitry has things under control as well. He makes sure the ordering and verifying and re-verifying of the complete order takes an eternity, thank God. Lapping away at Veronika, the guy has the tongue stamina of a porn marathoner. The poor girl's legs are shaking and quivering, her knees starting to buckle as she whimpers in orgasm. Veronika begs for him to stop. The Land Rover and line of cars behind us honk approval.

In between licks, Dmitry roars laughing and chews his cigar, then tosses down back deep pulls from his Kauffman Vodka bottle. A certified tongue master, there's a trail of slobber dribbling down his shirt. He's not just an investor. He's my new idol. He pulls a dildo out of his coat pocket and starts ramming it up her coochie. Viktor reaches an arm out from behind the blanket, and parks a thumb up her ass. They execute a precise dildo/thumb DP, alternating entry and exit rhythm to keep Veronika confused. Synchronized pumping. Russian teamwork at it's finest.

The clueless drive-thru monitor guy asks "will that be all?"
"yessss….yesSS! YESSSS!! YESSSSSSSSSSSSS!!!"
"Okay, thanks for jour order. Your total is XXXX rubles at first window. Please drive through."

As a bonus, after we pay, Dmitry makes Sascha exit the limo and stroll inside butt naked for some extra napkins. Quality stuff.

Fountain show at Moscow's Square of Europe

13.
SODOM AND GOMORRAH ORGY

Back at Dmitry's office, the entrance was ripe. The girls got out and strolled across the courtyard butt naked in their heels; McDonald's bag in one hand, bottles of Stolichnaya in the other, like it was the most natural thing in the world. Their beautiful ass-cheeks bouncing side to side to the rhythm of their quick strides. The scene screamed of cross-advertising potential. Regrouped inside the entertainment room, the three manly men sit on the rows of couches in front of the big screen playing a Jenna flick.

"I'm not eating that horsemeat" Dmitry barks at the girls, dismissing them with a waggling index finger back to the Jacuzzi. "I only eat catered delicacies Brett, I vas only kidding about McDonald's" with a wink. "Bring me a platter, honey. Da good stuff" he barks into his cell. After some shots and a round of jokes, a hottie in a French maid outfit appears and serves up a delicious spread. Fresh sushi and lobster, *kotlety* (beef-mince cutlets), carpaccios of salmon and tuna, and a teepee of Beluga caviar.

"Dust off da pool table, and lift joo skirt higher, for Christ's sake."

He removes a long glass vial from his inner pocket, and pours out two lines a half inch by twelve inches. Dmitry leans and does a vicious 7 inch snort like Keith Richards with horse nostrils. Viktor and I tap away. Lethal stuff. Having dined on pure golfball rocks in countless Medellin trips, I know the taste well. We devour the grub and candy like gold-plated cavemen. Eventually Dmitry waves the girls over, who inhale two 12" lines in minutes. He spanks and sends them back over to the corner to resume doing what girls do best.

Drinking and being bisexual sluts doing a stripper pole show.

"Viktor, put on some music. Some-zing loud and heavy. None of dat rap sheet. Seriously Brett, VOT da FOK is up with dat rap sheet. A bunch of retards mumbling out of key over sampled music. Ree-deekulus. " He pours a round of Kauffman premium shots.

"Dat reminds me. Brett; do joo know why Stevie Wonder and Ray Charles can't read."

"Why?"

"Because dere nee-gers." (rimshot!)

"I LIKE YOUR PANTS AROUND YOUR FEET, I LIKE THE DIRT THAT'S ON YOUR KNEES", Nickelback blasting through the Vandersteen speakers.

Viktor pops down on the couch. We form a business huddle. I use the opportunity to get more specific with Dmitry on business; the numbers, margins, liabilities and limitations on what to expect, and what we can and can't do on my end without complications. All three of us have been through the variations innumerable times, so it takes no more than five minutes till we agree on how the terms will fluctuate as the credit line usage increases. All in all, the meeting goes well.

The business was good.

The numbers looked good.

The pussy looked good.

Moscow is a cash city, and an obscenely corrupt one. Dmitry is presumably as legit as he needs to be. In this town, gangster connections are an added level of protection for doing business. The fear of political upheaval is very real. After the Yukos debacle, it forces men to make money fast, and move it out of the country even faster. This is Dmitry's forte, and the source of his latest fortune. He sets up offshore accounts, LLCs, trusts, and corporate shell companies. His services are lucrative and very desirable in this city.

"Brett, every time I blink, men approach me with duffel bags of cash to hide/wash for a substantial fee. Government officials are some of my best customers. Eetz funny how some defense ministers make 20K a year, and yet they have $5 million in rubles to hide."

Under communism, no one could own real estate. The transition to capitalism and private ownership is only in its second decade. Moscow is living in both the 21st and 19th century simultaneously. The money made in the last ten years in real estate is mind boggling. One thousand percent returns are common. NYC real estate is cheap by comparison. Dirty bankers and politicians, gangsters and caviar.

While the men talked business, the girls performed on the little stripper stage. Then they moved over to a full-on 69 show in the  Jacuzzi. Our meeting over, they towel off and make their way back to us. Not for our looks. We were hoarding all the liquor. Viktor had been assigned bartender duties, and made a dozen double Vodka Red Bulls that are going down real smooth. We spend an hour getting full contact lap dances, while binge drinking obscene amounts of assorted top shelf Vodka in a blistering pace. We polished off a token 2 cases of beer as a chaser. Highlights?

Despite being heavily lubricated, I passed on boning Dmitry's women. It's bad business. But to be a good sport, I did plenty of sleazy mauling, practicing bowling ball grips on them. The girls did this great little routine. One girl would sit on my lap with her back against my chest while spreading her legs, while another would get on her knees and lick her. Gorgeous tight firm young bodies, totally uninhibited, giving lesbian shows any man would be happy to pay for. Every few minutes Dmitry would clap his hands, and the girls would switch seats to the next guy. The girls were giggling and crawling all over us, beautiful ripe pulsating creatures of willing flesh in a scene reminiscent of Sodom and Gomorrah.

Eventually I move to my own recliner, where The King Brett blanket once again comes in handy. Dmitry lines up two girls side by side doggystyle, and starts undressing, signaling an orgy. I inform Viktor its time for me to leave.

Some rules for me are never to be broken. This is one.

Never be in the presence of another penis.

Viktor fires up the DB9, Britain's greatest gift to mankind, and gives me a hair-raising death cruise back to my hotel, during which we had Godsmack cranked just loud enough to make us believe we were singing in key. The ETA for tonight's pick up is exactly 10:15pm. He lets me off at my hotel and goes screeching out the driveway, while I secretly drool at his ride.

The hotties working the front desk bounce up and break out *We're horny* smiles. Blondes. Big Racks. I'm a frequent visitor at this hotel, with a healthy appetite for blondes with big racks and *we're horny* smiles. I walk to the desk. They make sure to turn around a few times shuffling papers from one side to the other for no reason, so I can see the creamy upper thighs peeking out from the ridiculously short skirts. Danilova, with the perky nipples and pearly whites asks "Will joo need late night room service tonight?" wink wink. (Brett did her last trip…a naughty little 'thang who likes it rough).

Out of their little welcome basket, I take a lollipop out, peel the wrapper off and run the candy down the length of her cute little pug nose and put it into her mouth.
"Not sure I'll be available. Think I should?" while picturing her tied and greased up with her ankles pinned behind her ears. She starts licking the cherry lollipop up and down until her tongue turns deep burgundy. Then, using her own hand she pushes the top of her head down and deep throats the whole thing.
"Only if joo like an all night sucker!" licking her lips.
    Staring at her mouth with a wandering mind, I start wondering if I really spent the afternoon gripping the luscious limo Lolitas like bowling balls. I sniff my fingers for confirmation and smile. I pick up another lollipop, peel off the wrapper and affectionately ram it in the mouth of the hottie next to her.
"Good things come in twos. Don't wait up for me honey…"

    As I walk to the elevator I feel their eyes burning a hole in my pants. I hustle up to the room for an hour of re-grouping and change of clothes into to the evening's stud-wear.
    We're going upscale tonight, trolling with Dmitry at Nightflight, the classiest and easiest place to hook up with the sexiest upper tier P4P women in Moscow. Viktor is due shortly, so I snag an armful of liquor out of the fridge and head downstairs.

14.
OLD SCHOOL MEETS THE
BEAST FROM THE EAST

Screaming pistons slice the dead summer evening air, as 20" tires strangling chrome rims come squealing up into the driveway. Obnoxious. Sleek curves. Ballsy and aggressive. But enough about me. Viktor valets his Aston Martin DB9 at my hotel, and pops out of the car wearing the vintage Russki scowl, while the car blasts *The Green Manalishi* in seven hundred watts of death and destruction.

"Are you kidding me, early Judas Priest? Nice pull. I can't believe you've even heard of that."

"Dere's no substitute for da vintage British metal."

"*…could use more cowbell*" adds the Johnson.

-   -   -

Damn I just love his ride. This is the big dog's luxury sports car, a modern slice of automotive heaven with a legendary history. Every Aston Martin is hand built. The cabin is pure British lavishness, with walnut burl veneer and hand sewn leather seating. It even smells rich. Underneath the stunning lines of elegance sits a growling V12. Nothing beats the class and exclusivity of a DB9. Hefty price tag though. (For a little less jack, Brett has the Jag XKR, a powerful, curvy beast of similar styling.)

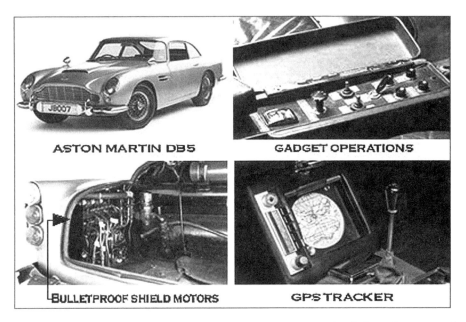

ASTON MARTIN DB5   GADGET OPERATIONS

BULLETPROOF SHIELD MOTORS   GPS TRACKER

My first Aston experience was many years ago. I had the pleasure of a 30 minute solo drive in the most famous Aston ever built; the Silver Birch DB5 in Goldfinger. They actually built four gadget cars, equipped with machine gun turrets, retractable bumpers, revolving license plate, rising bulletproof shield, etc. Of the two in the movie, one was wrecked, one survived. There were two additional cars that did promo tours. (I drove DB5/2017/R, -- one of the promo cars, the other DB5/2008/R recently sold for $2.4 mil). A right-hand drive sports car, the beefy engine is a bit sluggish off the line, but leaps on its hind legs as the torque ramps up; it had a mild shimmy at 105, but my drink was merely shaken, not stirred. The slow start off the line is not surprising, since that bulletproof shield that rises from the trunk lid is made of steel, and combined with the massive motors in the trunk added some 350 pounds to it. The gadgets operated from within the center console. Of note, it had a fake GPS tracker on the floor and phone in the door panel, considered absurd futurist dreams in the 60's. Aston Martin had some growing pains over the years, but they are back stronger than ever.

Like Lance Armstrong's support team, Brett meets Viktor with two six packs, a Snow Queen Vodka Liter and three champagne flutes. I drag him over to introduce him to the hotel's seasoned patriarch on the bench, for a few chuckles and time to kickstart the buzz. I see him several times a day and get a big kick out of his time warp aristocracy. Gramps is holding court with two well-dressed *dyevs* either staying at the hotel or working the lobby bar. While the ladies cheerfully respond to his banter, he sneaks glances up and down their shapely legs peeking out the miniskirts, twirling his shiny silver medallion like a kid playing with his first high school hard-on.

The guy is quite the charmer. First glance, you know he's a prolific storyteller. Every girl he's with is all smiles and respectful. As the ladies observe the younger lecherous dudes approaching with bottles of liquor, they shuffle on their way into the hotel, sneaking peeks back at us; oh yeah, they're working here all right. We approach the bench like defiant criminals facing the parole board.

I break out my best gravel voice, and introduce Viktor as Nick the Knife, and claim his grandfather is the guy who carved up Rasputin.

"That's rich, son. I must admit, I already know Nick and his black Aston. A fine motorcar indeed; waxed daily, chrome rims and custom throaty exhaust pipes. While you're entertaining ladies upstairs, he speeds up and down Tverskaya like a madman. Frankly he scares the hell out of me."

"*Dobrey den*. Pleased-a-to meet joo sir. I see joo don' miss a thing, no? I'm impressed."

"Pleasures all mine, son; whatever your real name is. I'm being a tad cavalier with you. This medallion around my neck is like a mirror. I saw you pull up. As for your cohort Mr. Gigolo comments, Rasputin was poisoned, shot, and drowned. But you knew I knew that, didn't you?

"Just testing your Alzheimer's pops" I confess, in a most sincere and condescending fashion.

"It would be our privilege if you'd humor us by indulging in some Snow Queen shots" as I pour us a round and hand him a flute.

"A most exquisite selection. Nostrovia, Gentleman."

Damn, the good stuff goes down smooth.

"Had a few to drink this evening young man?"

"Just a quick social twelve-pack to take the edge off. So pops, a small request from the peanut gallery. Perhaps you can share an old tale while we make a dent in this stuff."

The patriarch sits up in an instant, decadently cavalier and rigid, and immediately reaches into his archives and dusts off a classic back-in-the-day tale. Mission Accomplished. We have background noise while we chug our liquor.

The story is prolific and forgettable; his thick gray caterpillar eyebrows waggle as he shares each minute detail of his own rambunctious wildcatting with Russian ladies. I'd repeat a few details, but I didn't hear a word he said. That's what wise old geezers are there for. We nod our heads like we have rubber necks and attack the sixes and Vodka like there's a fire. 15 minutes, damage is done.

"Magnificent tale scrappy" I say while farting and monitoring my watch and beer level.

"Da vaay you describe them with such attention to detail… a true wordsmith. I'm thinking joove had a grand career in da theatre, no?" Viktor pipes in, pumping him with absurd grandeur.

"You really capture the essence of a seasoned cocksman" painting it thick out of defense, oblivious to the details of his story.

"Most gracious of you Brett, but I believe your parade of ladies in and out of this hotel is beyond my years. I must say though, you've got that look son. Some pigeons perch. Some are wanderers. You are definitely a wanderer."

"Touché. I must say, though, you have a look as well. You look like a women drove you to drink, and you didn't have the decency to thank her", a little microscopic glance into his soul. Viktor does all he can from busting out from his stone face.

"She never gave me the chance…" he replies with a huff, looking down and away. Oh oh. Touched a soft spot on that one.

"Are vee going to hug and sing Kumbaya, or can someone join me on a journey to da Carnal Palace of Lust?" growls Viktor, slamming the door on the inquiry with impeccable timing. Russians are known for their brevity. I pour the group a final round of three shots and raise a toast.

"To the Carnal Palace of Lust."

The old coot shakes his head disapprovingly, but reluctantly joins in. We slam them down, and head to the taxi stand.

"Be careful young man."

This is getting a bit much. With all this prolific advice, it weakens my breathless anticipation of reading about Oprah and Britney tomorrow.

15.
ARMED AND HAMMERED

Diving into a cab, the two fearless warriors head out into battle, carrying our company flag and ammunition of five imported beers, four blue Viagra, three French hens, two shot glasses and one liter of Snow Queen Vodka. Destination will be a pit stop at Pushkin Square. Hope that's enough. It must be a good eight minute ride. On the way, two upscale hotties in a black BMW Z4 convertible catch our eyes and follow alongside of us. Every pause in traffic, there they are with their frantic blond hair and over-inflated silicone racks and big huge smiles and "vere joo going babee" flirts out the window. This goes on for about five minutes of traffic, with enough peek-a-boobies, mwwah kisses and slurred sexual innuendos that they catch our attention for almost *three* seconds, while we compare recent brothel stories.

"Joo guys vont go drink und have sexy time vith us?!" says the tits.

"Are joo sure it vas a Donkey, Brett? Yea, whatever Bambi."

"Vere joo going, babee? Vee naughty girls, vee vant go vith joo now!?" boob flash, tongue lick, beer spill, head butt.

"From ten feet she shot darts with her poosie and popped balloons? I need to get out more often. Yeah. Yeah. Vats dat joo vant, Buffy? Joo vant deek?"

A piercing tire screeching slices through the air, followed by a seriously loud metallic BLAM! A car full of plastered farm girls rear-ends the beemer so fucking hard, the doors hung off their hinges like floppy beagle ears. Under normal circumstances we'd leap out of the cab and see if they were hurt. But seeing as their airbags were already deployed, well….

We finish the beers and a half liter of Snow Queen, and hand the remaining half bottle as a tip to the cabbie. He looked at the gift as if Moses had come down from the mountain with the tablets. We hop out in Pushkin Square. There's a huge crowd gathered. We squeeze in some dive club, where there's a live band blasting out astonishingly bad noise. Screaming Bad Metal. Devoid of any melody, controlled by a deaf sound man…it's so loud my ears may bleed. But the insanely packed crowd soaks it up and begs for more. Crowd surfing, vodka guzzling, and flathead fist pumping rage. It creates a flashback from my last band's high points; we were just like them, except the clubs were empty and we sucked. It's not that we weren't popular; it's just that we had a very selective fan base.

NIGHTFLIGHT

Address:　　Tverskaya Ulitsa, #17, metro Tverskaya.
Telephone:　629-1465
Restaurant: open 18:00-5:00
Nightclub:　 open 21:00-5:00.
Website:　　http://www.nightflight.ru/

Big hitter venue frequented by eccentric 8+ figure oligarchs, new money players, and cashed up tourists and expats. It's stuffed to the gills with high class gold-plated pussy. Nightflight also has a gourmet restaurant to please the sniffling sniffers with noses held high in contempt of peasants. To skip the line and cover charge, make a dinner reservation. Valet is swift, breezing us through feis kontrol with merely a token molestation by the security guards. A foreign passport sails you in as long as your threads are styling. We pause outside for a moment to take in the view.

The streets are overflowing with a frenzied paced attitude. Fast money never sleeps in the wild, wild East. Lines of high dollar Mercedes are valet parked in a row like a car dealership, their owners hunched over casino chips, cigars and heaving cleavage somewhere nearby. Scowling bodyguards escort trophy wives wearing enough diamonds they look like Christmas trees. Jewel-and-mink-draped models slither down the sidewalk with distant bored looks, pausing only to inspect their reflections in the windows of designer boutiques. A black Bentley Arnage and two Land Rovers are in a huddle idling nearby for a quick getaway, no doubt a gangster's entourage.

Porsche Cayenne and Bentley taxis awaiting Gangster billionaires

- - -

Uptown skyscrapers peer down on us with a corporate indifference. Despite the late night hour, the smoked-glass monstrosity windows are still bustling with activity inside. Stogies smoked while overnight Oil Futures positions are entered; dirty white chocolate martinis chugged reviewing Real Estate deals for the appropriate extortion clauses. In the penthouse office, while the secretary's head bobs under the CEO's desk, Natasha and Ivanka from VIPescorts.ru are booked for a threesome at the Marriott Tverskaya. The hours and stress can be brutal for der Russki corporate barons.

Across from the club entrance, a couple of inflato-lip cougars pushing 26 have been denied entrance, and summon us with hair flips, lifted mini-skirts and boob flashes. Sexy. Rough. Their darting eyes and coke noses twitch, as they impatiently wait for naïve wallets to appear. Sorry honey, do I look like I'm shopping for grannies? Brett's not in the mood to wake up next to a girl with a rose in one hand, dagger in the other, and a scorching case of herpes.

- - -

In line, being denied entry by the ex-military doormen is a posse of mutant poser warriors resembling Pixar animated bad guys. With multicolor spiked tops and shaved domes, they got neck tats that look like Freddy Krueger fungus rot, cutoff Affliction Tees exposing tatted 'roid biceps, and ugly smirking mugs in dire need of a flying brick. Rage, cheeseball, and bile alert. In a just world, these narcissistic tumors would be grinded into a fine paste and used as spackle behind a urinal.

"Here at the Moscow Special Olympics, every one is a winner," yells the Johnson.

Livid with rage in being denied club access, the circus posers push their luck a bit too far, and are told to GET THE FUCK OUT OF THE LINE and take a fucking hike NOW by a much fiercer group of enforcers with fists cracking and weapons slapping their thighs. Guard goons live for these moments, and play for keeps in Moscow.

The ladies? Feiz control rules this species as well. The sexier, taller and leggier they are, the better odds they'll be  hustled into the club. (dark alley BJs help with gray area rulings). With its buffet of leggy blondes in high platforms, Nightflight resembles the set of the Attack of the Blonde Amazons. As there's no sight of Dmitry's limo, Viktor and I cruise inside. Maybe Dmitry's taking laps at the McDonald's drive-thru.

We skip the restaurant and enter the nightclub and take a quick inventory. Sixty percent of the girls are 6.5-7.5+. A dozen are one-two o'clock on the erection scale. And a few primal lionesses that are pure Bad to the Boner. A nice selection for so early in the night. With wandering eyes and tent pants, we start slamming drinks like drunk retards in a Tijuana brothel.

- - -

In the cozy darkness, a corner table of prime real estate contains plastered Japanese businessmen in silk suits with cartoon grins, soaking up the voyeuristic oasis of cosmopolitan ladies on display. The Asian gents' dinner plates are swarmed with sushi, sautéed swordfish with nicoise vinaigrette, roasted duck and dark walnut chocolate cake. Another round of whiskey sours arrives, and are quaffed down in seconds and parked alongside multiple rows of half empty vodka martinis, each chugged and resting with two crisp olives still clinking the rim of the shapely glasses. The toasts come briskly, full of schoolboy giggles and permanent flashes of pearly whites in the direction of any and all Nordic goddess glances.

Tony Sony, a silver-haired gent of substantial means, is positively beaming as he stares at a hottie through tortoiseshell glasses with bloodshot puppy-dog eyes. Tony appears to be a ruthless T-Rex in the business world, ripping off estates of grandmothers, and during corporate takeovers hacking off heads and spinning them around by the spinal cord before tossing them into meat shredders. Judging from his uncharacteristic shyness, at Nightflight he's a lost babe in the woods, not having crossed that barrier of accepting the clarity and honesty of pay for play women. His ego just won't allow him to pay for it. Earth to Tony. We all pay for women.

The expensive ones (girlfriends/wives) we pay to stay. The inexpensive ones (the superhotts who fuck like racehorses) we pay to leave. Decisions, decisions. The concept of paying for it is killing Tony Sony. Confusion battling anxiety, he's all wide-eyed and circling the wagons, without an Indian in sight. His throbbing blue cahones are of no help, squirming around all feisty and tingly; screaming at him for being terminally shy.

Staring without blinking, he's so infatuated with one chick, he's holding his breath and turning purple. I follow his gaze. Ahhh. He's fallen for Aleksandra, a 6' Siberian seductress with machete cheekbones, a statuesque body and a timeless beauty.

Vivacious charisma. Explosive sexual attitude.

The pinnacle of Russian sensuality.

Horny Alek…a previous conquest of Brett. She took my sin, but she couldn't take my soul. Never happen. If you show a chink in your armor to a woman, they drive a semi-trailer through it.

I may have picked off a slice of hers, though. She still makes my toes curl just thinking about how spontaneously dirty she is in bed. She's perched near the gold railing, in a painted-on silk dress that clings to her like a second skin.

The swooping nightclub lights reflect of her glowing cheeks, while she licks her lips scanning the club. Her eyes light up, surveying me from a distance. Raising an eyebrow and crossing her arms at her chest, she speed taps her stiletto. I never call her to let her know I'm in town. It pisses her off. Sometimes it's tough to be distant with a scorcher like her, but I enjoy savoring the devious pleasure of an emotional and intellectual wall.

No complications.

Hmmm. Someone is a tad sensitive being without a client, merely eye candy for a table of 3-inch Japanese hard-ons. She tilts her head slightly, her gold flowing tresses falling over her right shoulder and seductively shielding half her face, giving her the look of a 50's femme fatale. Her ruby red mouth crinkles in a coy frown, and then she unleashes a heavy-lidded green-eyed smile that could melt the Alaskan tundra.

Bbooiinnngg.

"The nympho force is strong in this one" says the Johnson.

I t suddenly has gotten way to warm in here. Mesmerized, I sneak a peek back at her. Yummy. Brett has fond memories of dining on her boobie buffet; covered in whip cream, strawberries and honey . . licking her puffy areolas and dark walnut chocolate nipples, before stuffing a sweaty Viagra sausage down her throat.

She's looking boobalicious tonight too. The front of her dress is cut so dangerously low, the restaurant goes to Def Con 3. The manager keeps tabs on her with a look of terror. If just one of those perky high beams peek out above her lace bra, the walls  of the club may be sucked in from the sheer weight of her perfection.

"Down boy," I whisper to the Johnson. "We're looking for some strange tonight."

Either Tony Sony and I will start Kung Fu Fighting, or I need to be changing sides of the room and be free of her powers. Not in the mood for a repeat chick, I choose the latter.

Making my way to the john, I loop around past Aleksandra and grunt "*hey you sexy bitch*" in her ear while cupping her butt.

- - -

Perched on a barstool next to the Ukrainian wet dream is a gargantuan skank cougar, who thinks my flirting was directed at her; a sloppy American sista no less. (cue needle skidding across record with a deafening screech). Normally female monsters are invisible to me. But when something the size of a USC nose tackle with sandpaper hands grabs your arm in a vise grip, you take notice. Horrid face. Smells like the bottom of a Newark dumpster. A coal black water buffalo with some 'tude. Yikes.

"*Shit Buckwheat, I've flushed better-looking turds down the toilet*" says the Johnson.

Sitting in front of a bank of stage spotlights, when she shifts her donkey butt towards me, it forms a nightclub eclipse. Clearly the winner of the most out of place person in history. I'm not sure what her intended airline destination was, but wherever she was accidentally airdropped, it must have left one hell of a huge Ultra Sheen crater. She's got a massive pock-marked sumo wrestler's neck topped with a fro that looks like she got tossed from the eye of a hurricane and then lost a fight with a lawn mower.

Referring to my flirt to Aleksandra, she does da finger snapping head-bobbing thing. Then with Thunderbird and horse cock on her breath, she dishes out a sassy "oh no you didn't?!" in a deep James Earl Jones baritone.

"Well dAMN nigretta! Go on with your bAD sELF! Best be spENDING yo' next gANGbANG Benjamin on SOMe dental work, beeyotch. And uh…nice donkey butt."

I hold my breath and speed-walk towards the bathroom before she kicks my ass, while whistling the Theme from Shaft. As I pass his table, I lean over to Tony Sony. Pointing at his fantasy girl I encourage him, like talking to him like a five year old contemplating his first solo public urinal piss.

"Her name is Aleksandra, and she's available. Go to her Man. She's your density."

He doesn't hear a word. Peering down for companionship at the trembling martini glass in his hand, he looks like his period is late and he's going to cry. His friends slap him silly on the back and egg him on.

"Put a rubber on that big schnoz of yours and strut over to her. Tell her you give good nose." Roars, cackles, and chortlesnorts smack Tony's ego like Ed McMahon outtakes.

Suddenly, the Rocky theme starts roaring in his head. That's it! Squirming in his seat, he undoes the top button of his shirt while matting down his sweaty hair, and starts ahemming brusquely in her direction. Naïve to his superhero powers, Aleksandra chooses not to swoop over and get down on her knees. If he simply put his wallet on the table and did the come here finger, she may consider the offer and hop in his lap; Tony has to learn to crawl before he walks.

Returning from the pisser, I see the drunken, swooning Tony has pole-vaulted over the infatuation fence, and stands with slumped shoulders in front of the sleek, leggy goddess.

Damn. The girl just oozes sex.

She's a walking porno movie.

Any second you expect to hear *Pour some Sugar on Me* blaring through the house speakers, while she does a striptease covered in hot oil. Tony mumbles mangled inquiries in her direction, while meekly staring at the floor. She points to an imaginary friend across the room, and gallops away at a furious clip, using the last chance avenue of escape. All unknown to Tony.

While she bolted, Tony had been peeking back at his group table, in dire need of some macho credits and a liquid courage re-fill. After soaking up a healthy dose of "you da mans" and thumbs ups, he swivels back around with a cocky head tilt, only to find in her place a giant skinhead doorman with a condescending smirk of pain. He leers down at Tony flossing with a pick axe. Tony lets out a Junior High cheerleader yelp and cowers in retreat back to the boys, his tour of humiliation complete. I guarantee you he has an unemployed saddlebags wife who rides his ass like a military sergeant, despite her giving up on blowjobs three presidencies ago. Damn, he sulks to himself. Looks like another month of dating a Vaseline jar till the next Moscow run.

Despite the screaming loud techno and drunken chatter from the animated crowd, from 50 feet away I can still hear the gigantic ghetto sista. Damn. Her Fat Albert gut must start at her chin. Restless in her chair, she shifts to one side, moving a half ton of her gigantic bedonkadonk and it's minefield of ass zits, and waves the menu at some 80 yr. old (potential client?) screaming "you see this mutha fucka menu? Mad expensive shit!" to which grandpa nods and peels away, not interested in putting his little friend inside a snatch coated in dumpster juice that's as tight as the Lincoln Tunnel.

\- \- \-

Tonight, Viktor and I are with Dmitry, which means wining and dining with a handpicked fleet of A-list women. For expats and tourists, Nightflight is THE place for guaranteed hooking up in Moscow. For those of you in the minor leagues, who have only cruised the sports bar at Hotel del Rey in Costa Rica; your feet are wet, but you're missing out on the crème de la crème. When you walk the prime time gauntlet at Nightflight, 25-50 hotties line both sides of the narrow strip next to the bar. Tall blondes decked to the  nines eyeing your stuff up and down. Ass grabbing. Crotch stroking. Wallet sniffing. You feel like Brad Pitt the billionaire strolling through the Ms. Hawaiian Tropic dressing room.

\- \- \-

Dmitry finally arrives 30 minutes late, wearing a full-length black leather trench coat and matching wide-brimmed hat. Styling like gangster nobility in his threads, he gives a cynical little grin and shake of the head.

"*Dobry den*! Sorry for deez lateness, comrades. Fuckin' limo driver speeding again; got stopped by da rookie cop. No problems."

"Vi joo put up with dat sheet?" Viktor asks mildly pissed. "Joo have bought da entire force several times over."

Dmitry chuckles and waves his hand, Cuban Cohiba ashes flying in every direction.

"I could have pulled rank. Who's got time for trouble? I held him at bay with a few bottles of cognac and a promised high-end stripper after work. Before he left, I handed him da police chief's own beeziness card" as the club manager removes his black leather jacket.

"I said Velcum to da force. Next time call jour boss before joo even think of pulling me over." Viktor nods with an acquired smirk.

"I own him now, *and* he owes me. Beside, it's worth it just to see how scared he got."

After a huge belly roll of laughter, Dmitry walks past Tony Sony, flicks the tip of the cigar onto his shoes and parks us at the back two tables in the corner. Waiters sprint to his fingertips before Dmitry can even snap them.

He pulls the waiter close and playfully slaps him in the gut.

"Nikolai, the devil awaits! Bring da boyz enough bottles of Snow Queen and Kaufman Vodka and buckets of Carlsberg beer to make an entire rugby team pass out. Then refill eet every ten minutes. Get some girls over here too . . da good stuff" slipping him roughly $50US in rubles.

I swear it wasn't four minutes and four OMG face-melting, gorgeous giraffes and one average girl come prancing across the room in a beauty pageant strut, nestling themselves at our table.
The A-list of prime beef.

I recognize one as a showcase dancer. Another I remember from some Viktor porn emails, although I'll need to see her shaven snatch for verification. She was his cart girl last year at the Nightflight Open golf tournament. He told me he had 12 beers in 18 holes, and twice during the round he threw his ball in the woods and banged her stand-up doggie against a tree.

("Da second time vas a mulligan fuck.")

Dmitry squints with one eye and whistles to Nikolai the waiter, shaking his head pissed off. He sprints over with a petrified look, his brow drenched in sweat. Blue veins popping from Dmitry's temple, he waggles a finger sideways in his face in disgust.

"Nikolai, have I ever shown joo disrespect? Huh!" He pulls him by the collar down engaging him eye to eye, his cigar dragon breath baking into his face inches apart. He lowers his voice.

"Vats vith deez…vats vith deez plain girl? I told joo. Only da good stuff. Joo can't be bringing dat stuff around my table." He hands him a 1000 ruble bill, dismissing him with a mild slap of his cheeks followed by a finger gun.

Nikolai apologizes profusely and corrals the clunker chick out of her seat, hands her the 1000 rubles and hustles her away.

"Sorry about deez Brett. Nikolai eez not new here. He should know better."

A few minutes go by, and Nikolai returns with a top shelf black haired scorcher, her heels alternate clicking across the burgundy velvet carpeting and marble tile towards me. She sits on my left. My eyes make a quick inventory of the table's visual. The girls are stylishly chic. Exotic superlicious babes, with layers of flowing tousled hair covering their shoulders like a cape, and bodies worthy of sticky Penthouse pages. Juicy peek-a-boo racks. Impossibly thin yet curvy. The Johnson starts singing the Russian National Anthem. I run a cold beer across my forehead pretending I'm dizzy, while Viktor busts up and elbows me.

"Dmitry only buys the best" he whispers under his breath.

"Brett. I'd like joo to meet the Victoria Secret Lingerie team," Dmitry loudly bellows, blowing a swirling cigar plume towards the vaulted ceiling skylight. Let's forget da damn ceremonial name introductions, and get Yeltsin plastered off our asses."

Nods and winks go around the table. Having done five Ivankas, Dashas and Natashas in the last year, there's no point in me trying to remember any more names.

Cosmopolitan hott on my left looks like Ms. Universe. She literally takes my breath away. Crazy hot. Chiseled pinup body. She's has that rare sophisticated yet slutty aura… maybe a tad out of my price range. She clinks shot glasses with me. We slam them. She winks and gives me a fist bump (!), then grips my upper thigh and sticks her vodka-coated tongue down my throat. Well hello to you too, kitty. Classy always goes down well with dirty in my book.

I manage to extract her mouth from mine. Her rapid heavy breathes signal yet another Moscovian porn animal on the prowl. I lean back to examine her goods a bit closer. Piercing aqua-blue eyes with a mild Asian slant; not oriental, but the type common with Swedish and Estonia girls…they stare right through me with a warm sensual intensity. Her face is flushed, giving color to her sharp Slavic cheekbones dusted with light freckles. Tapered raised eyebrows and a curled puffy upper lip completes the CFM Penthouse pet face. Her sexual aura is energetic fire…I bath in it I experience it. I'm so possessed by it (and her ass) that I may have to pretend I'm listening in a conversation, dammit. She has on a silk body sheath of a dress that clings to her every curve, split high on the sides. She must have been dancing. Perspiration glues to her swollen breasts, her protruding nipples beckoning my serpent-like tongue, but settle for the inappropriate finger radio station dialing.

A three-quarter hard-on is lifting my corner of the table, so I make a nonchalant crotch adjustment to the side. Her eyes follow my hand. I catch her.

"I'm sorry; vell…not really," she says, doing a mild tongue lick around the outer rim of her pinkish red lips. I'm Dasha Svetlanavich, my friends call me Svetlana." Another tongue lick. I'm damn near popping a hole through my pants. Geez what a sexy bird.

"*Dobry den.* My pleasure. I'm Brett the Beast. My friends call me Brett the Beast."

"I know. I already know everyzeeng about joo, Beast."

-   -   -

Interesting. So much for thinking I've been stealth over the years. Not sure if the reputation is good or bad, nor do I care. I set my standards low, and then go way below them. We share small talk for a bit. Drink a few shots. Little strokes back and forth under the table. Enjoy the repartee and amusing sparring retorts traveling around the table. She shares her story; a part-time runway model, recently broke up with a wealthy oligarch, she was valedictorian in college, studied ballet, speaks three languages, and has an insatiable appetite for cock.

Pressing my body against her, I mention my business with Dmitry, and share a bogus fascination of Russian architecture, theatre and the arts. She purrs, and kisses me every other sentence. In between rude sexual innuendos, I accidentally mention my sold out European classical piano tour, my Formula F1 team and private 767, and the crème de la crème, my fine collection of hot wheels cars, bongs, and soiled cheerleader panties. The clincher is when I lick my eyebrows. She breaths heavy moans on my neck, and whispers dirty little nothings in my ear. I lean away offended, wink at the other girls, playing hard to get. She runs a hand up and tickles the rod before settling with warm fingers placed top thigh.
Like candy from a baby.

Svetlana excuses herself for the bathroom. I figure it's either for a quick toot, or she just wants me to check out her bod to close the deal. Though painfully low slung in the front, her classy dress is high neck, inviting curious eyes. As she climbs over me and stands, my pulse races to insane levels, like Neil Peart doing a drum solo on crystal meth. The dress is backless. Its cut so low in the back, the top of her bootie is peeking out. My eyes follow the athletic back cleavage curve up her long torso, and race back to her bootie.

From five paces, she turns back and locks eyes with a grin and busts me with my tongue resting on the floor. To complete her voyeur tease, she shifts back towards me and bends her whole body across my lap to rescue her purse. I get the full view down her dress. A treasure trail of blonde hairs cascading down her back cleavage into the tiny-hiny crack. Brett's kryptonite. And no panties.

Bbooioinngg.

-   -   -

I peek down inside the back of her dress and see a scrumptious bubblebutt so tight, you could bounce a quarter of it and two silver dollars would bounce back. Viktor and I catch each other's eyes drooling down at her stuff. We both mouth "I'd hit that" and cackle away like newbie schoolboys.

Svetlana giggles, and moves across the tile floor in a stiletto power strut so sensual it could unleash a downpour in the Sahara Desert. Off in the distance I see Tony Sony ogling at her, beads of sweat pouring like a river down his forehead, his nervous ass glued to his seat. Seeing as its six martinis later, he just may gets his nerve up enough to offer Svetlana $500 to come in her purse and run for the hills.

I scan across our table at the host. An even hotter girl is attached to Dmitry like a Siamese twin, puffing away on his cigar, with one hand under the table making the cloth rise and fall. Her long eyelashes flutter like a golf umbrella opening, her soft vacant eyes admiring him with a bewildered lust. It's nice when they come so well trained. I give her the gentlemanly tip of the champagne glass, while picturing her blowing me in the religious section of the public library while I'm dressed as Ronald McDonald.

Viktor leans in and whispers.

"Brett; I swear to God, Dmitry's chick has an IQ of one."

"Perfect. It makes it easier to fuck her brains out. I mean, how long could it take?"

-   -   -

In the entrance to the nightclub stands an impeccably dressed man in a perfectly tailored suit, with a cagefighter's mug and thick sculptured hair. His small entourage is three scowling gorilla bodyguards. Mr. Big takes a few strides into the nightclub and sets up shop standing next to the bar, while an incoming swarm of gorgeous *dyevs* invades his space in a blitz. Barely noticeable, a non-descript frail dude walks by palming a digital camera, taking a quick snapshot of the group, before making a hurried beeline towards the door. A bodyguard spins and picks him up off the ground by his belt and his hair, and flings him headlong into the wall. The camera bounces, but remains intact on the floor. Guard two smashes the lens to pieces with his jackboots.

Dazed and bloodied, the weasel casts a wide-eyed terrified glance at the big man with tears streaming down his face, and then ambles towards the exit with a limp. Guard three snatches him like a rag doll and lifts him airborne with one hand. The weasel fingers the sleeve of his roughshod coat and mumbles something hysterically. The guard wrinkles his nose with clenched teeth, his face clouded with anger as he catches the boss's glance. Mr. Big shakes his head no. The guard releases him with a grin and fakes a face punch. Weasel exhales a massive sigh of relief, and stumbles deliriously out the front door leaving a trail of Hershey squirts in his wake.

"*Hasta la vista, baby*" snickers the Johnson.

I lean over to Viktor.

"Let me guess, KGB turned energy gazillioniare?"

"Da. Top dog of Kremlin internal security a few years back. Now, he's a raw materials and shipping magnate. He owns controlling interest in da second largest aluminum and steel manufacturing plants. We call him metal man. Bad guy to be on wrong side of."

It's the vintage thumbnail biography of numerous oligarch centimillionaires in Moscow. Their bios are a joke. They go from pushing a broom at McDs to Bill Gates in five years, with no coherent transition. "Boy; that Boris really applied himself." Nobody knows how extensive their holdings are, how they got them, but somebody is always angling for a piece of them. In a throaty whisper, The Johnson says "*Michael, we're bigger than US Steel.*"

-   -   -

Svetlana returns and does the same torturous crawling thing across me and sits. Dazzling sensuality. Devious mind. Her eyes twinkle as I peek down at her Slavic party pack. She catches my look of deviance, and instinctively hikes her dress up and parts her wheels a bit, the tops of her lace stockings in plain view.

Beautiful legs. Long. Thin. Sleek, like the Cigarette speedboats at the nearby gangster marina.

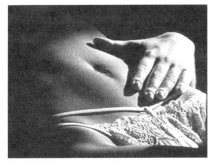 I run the tips of my fingers up from the knee and pause at the top of her thigh, and a soft moan escapes her lips. Her skin is flawless; soft and velvety smooth. Geez. She's steaming down there. I nearly burned my hand. She ruffles the hair on the back of my head, and runs her warm fingers through it. She leans close and kisses my neck, her female hormones and fragrance damn near intoxicating. Turning my head to hers, she starts kissing me passionately again. The Johnson starts head butting the zipper, making it damn near impossible to sit still.

"So, are you a born nympho, or a great actress trying to land a filthy rich man?" Brett asks, picturing her in an AA meeting riding a

Budweiser shaped Sybian with thick white stripes in her hair.

"I like joo. I vant to do things to joo" she coos in my ear with an early Bondish panache, leaning forward with a puffy nipple peeking.

"Well honey, I'm not rich…but I'm definitely filthy."

Wink. Sneer. Looking away bored, I check out the feline competition on the dance floor. Build up a little tension. It's never too early to fuck with women. There's a multicultural babe on the floor in a near transparent sarong dancing real sensual, a sea-foam green thong clearly visible through the thin fabric. She's flipping her waist length hair side to side. Lips puckered. Her hard nipples are visibly pushing against the see-through material. Pupils dilated, her eyes floating ethereally lost in the music. Time stands still as she baths her veins in vodka and ecstasy pills. Someone needs to yank her back to a room and enjoy the ride.

"Dat's not what I hear. Aleksandra says you're both" Svetlana giggles, with the cutest little gotcha smirk.

It wasn't till that moment I noticed Aleksandra was sitting at our table three girls down, her jealous eyes bouncing off me and my new friend like pinballs.

"Do joo vant to know why I like joo?" Svetlana says with a wandering finger massaging the crotch.

I say nothing and put a finger on her lips with a sshhhh. I'm like the Clint Eastwood of porn here.

Kissing my neck with a sensual urgency, her breathing comes in short nasal spurts, her giant eyelashes tickling my cheeks. Zipper is opened, and warm fingers crawl inside. Normally I'm picky and spend hours choosing the perfect girl for the evening. Tonight, it takes all of five minutes with Svetlana and it's a done deal. One down. One blonde to go.

With one girl taking care of, my liver is screaming for attention. As the afternoon buzz is long gone, I'm ready to get ripped in a hurry. When landing babes is this easy, it's important to stay focused on the drinking. Russian women need no invitation to do the same, as they're born binge-drinking sluts. Next thirty minutes, I throw back a olte polite six-pack and five shots without anyone noticing. Then I pick up the pace.

Dmitry's tales are the center of attention. Central themes include his hilarious infatuation with embarrassing public blowjobs, forcing S&M lesbians on virgins, and nude pole dancers during corporate meetings. He tells of pussy shopping trips, parking his limo outside high schools in the provinces and hiring girls for $200 a week under the condition that they can't wear clothes for seven days.

"$200 is like 10 grand to them, Brett," Dmitry adds. "After a week of gourmet meals and top shelf vodka, I can't rid of them. They vant to do more perverted things den I ever think of!"

Perfectly timed, an enormous cheer fills the club, as the showcase dancers start grinding their stuff on the stage. Staring at their smooth cameltoes, I think back to the Limo Lolitas climbing all over me at McDonalds; not sure if I ordered it, but my pants were covered in cameltoe sauce.

I wink at Viktor. Every Moscow trip he and I do blitzkrieg jaunts for girls into the provinces; we have one scheduled in a few days.

Viktor elaborates.

"The verd has gotten out about Dmitry. Dere such a long waiting list of province girls for hire, he and I hold Barely Legal couch auditions. Most are sent home to Mom in the limo with a gangbang souvenir bottle. Dey walk like dey just got offa der horse."

Despite all this macho sex talk, the girls laugh and take it all in stride. Try pulling that off in feminist hell back home. Russian girls. As long as you feed them drinks and they hook up, they're the coolest party buddies you've even had.

Yes sir. Dmitry loves his story telling, and covers the table with a gourmet spread to keep our mouths from stealing his thunder. Heaping plates arrive with Georgian lamb, luscious sturgeon and sterlet interlaid with fresh lemon slices, sautéed duck foie gras, gilt-rimmed bowls topped with fresh cherries, shrimp and crab; even a small pyramid of Osetrova and Beluga caviar. Quite the spread. We gobble it down with our fingers and wash it all back with shots, like homeless alcoholics posing as restaurant critics. For desert he passes out a dozen one-hitter gram vials of pure blow, which turns the ladies into chattering parakeets, comparing stilettos, plastic surgeons, dick sizes, and solving world peace. I wink at Viktor and point a finger gun to the temple. Ear plugs please.

Throughout all the tales, Dmitry keeps filling champagne flutes of Kaufman and Imperia vodka, and the girls keep tilting them back in one gulp. Gulp, snort, chug, snort snort. Over the next hour and a half, after at least 20 shots, the girls are completely unfazed. Like it's water. Viktor has been doing one and sometimes two to their one, and shows no visible signs. As smooth as Russian vodka is, Brett is not a 20 shot guy, and is struggling in the mid-teens. Kleenex please.

With the girl on my right now warm and cuddly, my hands are very occupied, while the crotch is getting a massage under the table. On a positive note, a vodka brain freeze has taken hold. When the girls speak to me, their lips are moving, but only a muted dial tone reaches my ears. Excellent. Since I can't hang all night with these

straight vodka lunatics, it's back to Double AA ball for me. Like King John Daly said, "I quit drinking. Just beer now."

Brett grew up on beer. Twenty beers in a day is no big deal. (spoken in a deep southern drawl)...aw hell, that's just *drankin*.' I need to follow Daly's sage advice, or I'll be doing stupid human tricks. (The ghost of John Belushi shakes head in disgust.) A cold Unesco in one hand, a perky rack in another, the night continues.

Dmitry grabs the waiter and signals for two expensive bottles of wine, the years and brand since lost in my brain freeze. As they arrive, Dmitry has the waiter pour a glass for me for the taste test. I raise the glass and toast the esteemed group of wealthy degenerates.

"Allow me to treat you to a ring seat to view my liver's demise."

Everyone raises a glass. I replace mine on the table, snatch the bottle out of the waiter's hand and chug for a good five seconds.

"Vat do you think Brett," Dmitry cackles through swirling cigar smoke with a juvenile delinquent's grin, his bald head glistening.

"The first hundred dollars went down a little rough, but it smoothed out after that. Dmitry, I'm thinking the occasion calls for Zubrowka Martinis."

"Da! An excellent call Brett" snapping his fingers without looking for Nikolai the waiter.

So much for slowing down. Feeling no pain now, which means obscene comments and sticky fingers are right around the corner. I grab a few champagne flutes and manage only partial success in trying to fill them. A hott grabs the bottle from me with a *Nyet!* She chugs directly from the bottle, and passes it to the other girls. A hand takes mine and moves it below the table. I feel my index finger being put in a warm honey hole. Svetlana cups my chin and turns my head, and it's back to sucking face again.

"So babeee. You *are* going to leek my poosie tonight, yes?" with the innocent raised eyebrows of a librarian. She lifts my hand from under the table and sucks on the sticky index finger.

"I vant switch seat now!" gets yelled from across the table.

Oh oh. Aleksandra's jealously has officially peaked. She demands exchanging ringside seats with my neighbor blonde on my left…who gives me a vat joo vant look.

Brett sniffs his sticky finger, approving of the sweet musky scent.

"Svetlana stays. You in the blonde, switch with her."

The girls stand and do a Chinese fire drill seat change dance.

"What da hell, Alek? Quit the pouty faces and bring that warm coochie over here for Daddy," I say with a heartfelt paternal desire for her emotional stability and reverse cowgirl. The girl has a bad case of slut eye for me, and needs a curing. She nuzzles up beside me, with wandering hands all over me like a horny octopus.

"Looking delicious tonight, baby. Love that dress on you."

"Joo should. Joo bought it for me last time in town."

"I did? Damn, I've got good taste. So why didn't you go home with Tony Sony? It looked like a match made in heaven." Time to mess with Alek.

"Da! More like match in hell. Vat a *pizdyuk*! (pussy). Und vot eez dat old man thinking? I dawn fuck fossils for free!" spits the sexy capitalist, while twirling her hair and running her fingernails up my thigh to the zipper.

"Too good for Japanese money, are we?"

"Brett, I vant to get fucked, not tickled. Jour pinky finger eez beeger. I go only von time with Japanese. After two minutes of him fumbling around between my legs, I ask him eez it in yet, and he starts coming! Ree-deekulus."

"So what happened then?"

"Joo wouldn't believe. Vee verr in da car seat; he fell asleep on my chest. I couldn't move. After half hour of snoring and farting, he wake and vee verr stuck together by his dried sperm on my stomach."

"OK, I'll bite. What happened then?"

"Eventually we peel away a few layers of skin when we finally separate. A veek later, I find out da Sumbitch gave me da crabs!"

Zippppp. I feel her fingers stroking inside my pants now under the tablecloth. Her story complete, she settles down and seems to have matters in hand.

"In case I forget to tell you Aleksandra, I had a really great time tonight" tapping her on top of the head with one hand, running my fingernails inside her upper thigh with the other.

"Joo twisted, Brett. I like dat. A smart ass eez much better than a dumb ass." She squeezes my rod hard for a second making me gasp, and then resumes the mild stroking with a giggle.

"Joo miss me? Huh? Do joo? My poosie miss joo. Joo do sexy things to me last time. Dees time, I vant to do naughty things to you."

"Stand in line."

"Brett. Joo think I jealous? I no care. Two girl, three girl, no matter to me. Admit it. Joo miss me. I see how you eyes linger on me. Joo know. Joo have that look." Snort..snort, tongue lick, vodka chug.

"Two girl sounds fine to me. You like Svetlana, yes?"

"I like."

Svetlana hands Alek an X pill, which they swallow with dirty grins, tonguing their lips at me.

Business is going quite smoothly tonight.

In the midst of this non-stop drinking and hooking up fun, a greasy storm cloud invades the space above our table. Sub-humans that dwell below pond scum, even below attorneys. It's a cocky euro-poseur and a slimy Jersey douchebag leering up and down at our women, their feet shuffling and bouncing in place like spoiled brats who have to pee.

"Yo, waDDUP. Juice guys are hogging all the da hot chix, ehhh," in that unmistakable loud, slurred voice of a Guido.

"A'ight, mang. Straight up playa keepin' it real, ya diGGGG."

Viktor immediately loses it and bounces up out of his chair. He's a 3rd degree black belt with a really short fuse and doesn't suffer idiots lightly. I grab his arm with a nod and tell him to let it play out. I love a great public humiliation moment.

Joisey has a greasy forehead that is tanning booth orange, below cactus-spiked hair coated with W10-40…da good stuff. A lousy fighter with an IQ of a brick, his classic fat pizza face with the Terminator square-jaw is dented out of alignment, costing him his dream career as a crash test dummy. Da Vinster is stylin' in an absurdly tight Dolce & Gabbana tee borrowed from an 8 yr. old, an unbuttoned shiny gold Chess King shirt, and $200 vintage artfully shredded jeans that people threw out in dumpsters 15 years ago. His Flavor Flav fake gold watch with a spinner rim is the size of the Big Ben clock. Bling upon TattZ upon megaBliNG$. FaGEDaBoudit!

Our table ignores his smug stupid-ass grin with a stone-faced silence. A frantic gum smacker, saliva dribbles into his chinstrap beard, while he adjusts his three-incher every two seconds. He getz props and High Five credits from his euro-bro' for bUSTING da aGGressiVE move on da chix, yo'. Eurotrash does a two second Michael Jackson dance move and scratches his coke nose, then remembers Vinnie's crotch grabs prior to da FIVE. He sniffs his hand. (That's strange(?)….it smells like ass).

Neanderthal alert. Cartoon creepy. Possibly 2nd generation upright in the family. Vin Man takes a deep hit of grape soda from his Scarface sippy cup, and continues WADDUP workin' it yo', displaying an overrated self-worth that is astonishing.

"Shi' mang, dey fly beetches creepin' in da house, yo! Deez bitches are off tha hook! Looka doze fawkin' KNAWKas! Hey, how YOUS doin', ehhh?" offering an olive-oily handshake to Aleksandra while sneering with fake pucker lips. She slides back five feet in her chair like he's got the Bubonic Plague, while doing the finger in the mouth vomit signal to the girls.

"He looks like a retarded chimp," Svetlana says to Alek, busting the whole table up.

Eurotrash Pierré von Dickbreath is all head-tilting wassup, duded up, jelled up, and popped collared up, with six buttons of his Armani silk shirt undone. With layers of rosary beads and puca shells bouncing off the orange shaved chest, he's as narcissist and pretentious as a 5'5" poseur can be. He looks like a slimy radioactive lizard. He's spewing so much Axe cologne and Taco Bell breath, he may melt the silk plants behind us. Somehow he's oblivious to da Vin smackdown, and is looking to one up him using his imaginary street cred. With his post-modern intellectual raised eyebrow, he leans in to dish out some faux bourgeois speak, only to find two of the hotts with raised palms saying "talk to da hand" while howling in laughter.

Fucking hilarious.

"Viktor, we're no match for our girls."

"Da! Russian girls are brutal."

But a guido is a guido. Shameless. Classless. Beyond annoying. Da Vinster just *knows* his imaginary charm and GQ looks will make a Russian model beg to move into his parent's basement at Turdy turd and tURD in da bRonX. Dat's right. Vinnie is a da bomb, showing up big tonight, rolling with a fresh half G off daddy's stolen credit card. It's a long way from his summer job picking up cig butts at Jilly's Arcade on the boardwalk at the Seaside Heights beach. Both dorks are walking caricatures of themselves. In five years Vinnie will be taking a dirt nap in a Coney Island dumpster, while Pierre bobs for dinner in an East Liverpool porta-john.

"So, are juice guys named Neil and Bob, or is dat just what you DO, OHHH?" Brett tosses out a little Dice in da house.

"*Your ego is writing checks your body can't cash*", says the Johnson settling the score.

"Hey, ehhhh. Juice gottz two extra blondes, you know what I'm f-f-f-friggin' saying!" Vinnie blurts out nervously, beads of perspiration pouring down his orange forehead. His skin looks like he sleeps in a toaster. With his midget short arms flapping and feet bouncing wildly, he looks like he's running in place.

"Drop it like it's hot, sistas. Yous chix in da mOOD for some rEAL men or WHAaa?!," Vinnie slobbers, bobbing his slimy spiked head so violently some pepperoni flies off and slides down von Dickbreath's silk shirt.

"A'ight dogg, doin' it straight up DEE-troit style," Eurodouche slimes out with his own vicious quick head tilt, splashing vinegar in da Vin's eye. He's also getting extra nervous, as sweat is blurring his wigger talking points tattooed on the back of his hand.

"Dmitry. It stinks in here. Please take out da trash," pleads one of the girls.

"Hmmm? Oh. Sorry girls. GREASEBALLS! Get fucking lost before my boys carve you up like a fish," Dmitry says with a snap of the fingers, puffing on his Cohiba without looking up.

The manager runs over with the fear of God in his eyes. He points the douchebags' eyes to Dmitry's giant bodyguards cracking knuckles in the corner, and waves a no with his index finger in the idiots' face. Leave. Now. Or die.

They speed walk away without looking back, trailing an oil slick like pregnant snails.

Can I have the last 5 minutes of my life back?

-    -   -

Time to change the mood. I do a toast to Dmitry, pump him with softball questions to get his ego going, and then challenge him for more juicy and graphic stories. He's more than happy to hold court. It's fascinating to watch him and the other mega-millions gangsters in action. Moscow is all about business, flash, and status symbols. Earn as much fast money in a short time and spend it or hide it all, before someone steals it from you. You'll see five women surrounding one man, feeding off a five thousand dollar tab, and the guy doesn't blink an eye. He isn't expecting sexual favors in the least. It's literally the equivalent of ten bucks to them. The girls have to force themselves on them to get laid; like the girl next to Dmitry is.

"Dmitry, let's shine your cue ball head with turtle wax and go bowling head first," Viktor says, always hilariously abrasive and in the face of anyone within listening distance.

"Bwahhaahaaa. Viktor: you're talented, driven, and always exceed expectations when it comes to beeziness. I'd like to tell joo from da bottom of my heart, that you're irreplaceable…BUT JOOR NOT! Bwaahaaahaaaaa!," Dmitry spits out with vigor.

- - -

Trying to gain access to our table, a slightly wobbly redhead in a seriously tight red dress hovers nearby. Vivacious. Horny. Hammered. All the necessary bonk ingredients. About 5'11" in her heels, she has gorgeous long curly auburn hair and green beacons for eyes. A tight bum presses against the silk, and a large swinging rack begs to break free from the low cut dress. Clearly available for inspection to the nearest set of paws. Fucking slamming body. You know why redheads always have great bodies? They have to. They're redheads.

"Nice to meet me honey," Brett says to the eager and playful new entry, while picturing her on her knees bobbing up and down on my rod, balancing a plate full of fries and a greasy burger on her head. I run my hand way too high up her thigh, and playfully spank her ass.
"Hi Beast, joo remember me?"

The blondes at the table hiss *ne Nado* (don't!) at her like rising cobras at the intrusion. Rred turns a heel in her rapid escape. Hmmm. Can't say I remember the face, but her ass looks vaguely familiar. Next.

Svetlana asks for more wine. Peering across the table, there's only one bottle left, on Dmitry's side of the table. That's odd. A quick pan and I see Aleksandra has turned sugary and languid. Her eyes are heavy-lidded with a diabolical glow. I lean over and she puts her head on my shoulder, in an unusual quiet moment. A faint whimper. Shortness of breath. I lift the table cloth up. OMFG! Legs trembling.

Panties resting on her stilettos. Her hand is buried between her thighs under her skirt, pumping the wine bottle in and out. Barely concealed tremors, as she hits the G-spot in the middle of a classy club. I swear the sophisticated *dyevs* are dirtier than the strippers and uber-punk whores in the rape-me-now clubs.

"Sorry babee, I no can wait," as her pace quickens, riding the bottle while eye-fucking me before a deep French kiss. This little crazed nympho moment sears into my mental hard drive. When it comes to sex, Alek is an explosively Russian soul. Not one to interrupt a woman, I observe the table porn in secret. Svetlana forgets the wine and gets a vodka shot, and chirps with the other girls.

A few minutes of bottle lust pass, and Alek is panting with shallow lungs, eyelids closed making the O face, her hair strewn across her

cheeks in a raw porno slow-mo. I manage to convince her the bottle will never be monogamous. She pulls it out with a high-pitched squeal and sighs. Arched upward during this dildo initiation, it still has enough left to fill a wine glass. I snatch the bottle from her.

"Don't forget to call me," Aleksandra slurs with fake puppy dog tears, blowing the bottle a kiss.

Brett picks up Svetlana's wine glass, and waving the bottle in a pretend pour motion, asks if she still wants some. She yanks the bottle away from me, and guides the bottle slowly to her full pursed lips for a finishing chug. Brett has a chuckle to himself. It's the little things.

A round of absinthe drinks arrives at the table, aiming to obliterate whatever brain cells are left. After our particularly thirsty evening, one glass of this death mix is the equivalent of taking a sledgehammer to your head. Great stuff. Highly recommended. Goes down well with handcuffs and totaled cars. The Johnson leans over to Svetlana and says "*honey, would you mind putting a leash on the Beast's liver, I've got work to do tonight.*" I glance across the table at my wingman, Viktor. His two hotties are batting their eyes at him in a look of profound affection, deep pools of soulful romance in their eyes...well at least several hundred dollars worth. The DJ is blasting 80's cheeseball classics. Dmitry climbs up on his chair, gnawing away at his cigar threatening to sing. Officially hammered, the Victoria Secret Lingerie team in a group power-snort finishes the rest of the blow in the one-hitters and rises, breaking out into an impromptu synchronized dance, singing I WANT YOUR SEX! by George Michael. A tit pops out here. Crotch shot here. Lezzie  kiss there. As for the men in the crowd observing the show ...a hard-on here, chin drool here, wet fart there. The potential for nudity is imminent. I elbow Viktor and do the slash neck signal to leave. Left to their own devices, our classy models will be dancing on tables shedding clothes any second now. He agrees. Take me drunk. I'm home.

"Brett. Right about now, joo and I may have an IQ of 1."

"Be strong, Viktor. Don't let them fuck your brains out without a fight."

Dmitry insists on paying for the tab AND the girls, so Viktor and I throw out a $250 each in rubles for the tip.

"*Charge it to the Underhills*" yells the Johnson...he's officially hammered by now.

"Viktor, joo take deez two blondes, Brett...joo take the two girls pumping your deek...and honey, looks like you won da Dmitry lottery. Vatz joor name again?...ehhh, never mind."

This ends up being the last thing I remember.

"Igor. Eetz Natasha. I be late for dinner. Da car stuck in pothole."

16.
NATIONAL PORNOGRAPHIC

Five hours later, I wake up in the hotel room john. Complete absinthe blackout. Oops. Apparently I fell asleep doing an old man sit down number one. First thought; where am I? Panning the room, the thought process begins. Looks European. Prague? No, too shiny and medieval. Maybe Russian? Definitely Russian. Kiev? No, too gaudy...definitely Moscow. Wait, I know this hotel. A horsefly bites my thigh and flies away in drunken loops, plummeting to its death screaming *"joo bastard"* in a death curdle. I take a sober up shower and get ready for a favorite event every trip.

Time to see what Brett has won in the bedroom lottery.

Strolling out into the room, iridescent light flickers out of the corner of my eye. The lap top is on, and the futures trading platform and charts are loaded up. Oh Shit. Definitely no memory of that. In a hurry, I check to see if I have any open positions. Positions panel shows I closed out 5 euro contracts for a $780 profit. Sweet! Drunk daytrading pays for the evening again. (a side gig for a dozen years now). I close down the platform and laptop, and turn to see what's under the covers.

I actually get a kick out of this portion of the blackout routine, having done it many times. The bed sheets are pulled back to see what hotties I pulled the previous evening. Two scorching amazons intertwined naked. Perky tits. Gorgeous faces. Six-pack stomachs. Tight asses begging to be plowed. Yes! (*bow chika chika bow bow*)

I recognize Alek. The other one looks vaguely familiar. No memory of the first session in the least. No worries. Easy to take care of that. I wake them up with a few licks, and they are ready to go at it again, like spring lovers in heat.

Threesomes? Done so many I can't count. They are either great, or really great. Some girls hide in the bathroom while you do the friend. Some sit at a distance in a chair, with legs crossed, top leg bouncing madly while they watch and wait their turn. These girls are just what Brett the Beast would special order. Very bi. And very dirty.

I cover the bed with towels and convince the girls to give me an oil massage. Four hands stroking and fondling, with greasy naked bodies sliding up and down mine. While certainly no match for a Bangkok Soapy, it does manage to wipe out some of the morning cobwebs. Then I take turns massaging their beautiful lean bodies.

As the sunlight peeks through the blinds, the view of their oiled up buns in a line is breathtaking. But what I want first is to see them use toys and then do each other.

While they start kissing and caressing each other, I reach into the bedside drawer and pull out a velvet pouch. The sex party pack.

Inside are glass dildos, rabbit vibrators and assorted lube and toys. Airport security knows this party pack well. Like clockwork, Brett is always the guy stopped at customs. Once again, this trip the rabbit was the most closely inspected item. A very large scary woman with a striking resemblance to Brian Bosworth held it, rotated it, and sad to say, fondled it with deeply introspective concern. When asked, I say it's a back massager, which is like calling a bicycle a toothbrush. It gets handed back without a word. I make sure to look down so I don't see the creepy sex smirk from the Boz. When I reach my hotel room, I put on an astronaut suit and spend hours cleaning the rabbits with hydrogen peroxide, a voodoo bonfire, holy water, and bow down and beg forgiveness for the inappropriate beast paws.

-   -   -

The girls open up the party pack, and go straight for the rabbits. It's the top of the line rabbit: it burrows into multiple holes simultaneously, has swirling pearl beads that go forward and reverse in 9 speeds, dual motors, g-spot stimulator; it vibrates and has this twirly-bird thing going on. It's like a portable vibrating circus. You need to kick start the damn thing.

After several minutes of testing each function, the girls figure out the perfect angle. Brett assumes the video director role. I have them lying back propped up by pillows, bodies side by side with their legs spread wide facing me. One leg crossed over the other girl. Eyes locked on mine. A free hand stroking up and down each others clit. Rabbits enter in and out vibrating, thrusts meeting each stroke, hair flying and thrown back with throaty moans. Erect thick nipples poking out like bullets from their rose-colored areolas. It's the show I fly halfway around the world to see. Takes about 90 seconds for the first round of explosive orgasms, and they continue non-stop after that. Convulsions – screams – legs shaking – practically hyperventilating in ecstasy, as a tear flows down their cheeks. The rabbit is the truly the pimp daddy. I even put ESPN on mute during the finale. Tent pole arrives on cue. I mount up and do each girl missionary back and forth a half dozen times like the crazed beast that I am. Another quiet morning turns into an exotic fuckfest.

Session highlights?

The girls were in the 69 position going at it. Saddling up doggiestyle, I'm drilling Alek's cinnamon ring, while underneath my rod Svetlana is licking her juicy lips; Alek is flicking her tongue on Svetlana's clit. Alek is soaking wet. Looking down I watch a steady stream of juices drip down from Alek's pussy into Svetlana's open mouth, who drinks it all up. Then out of nowhere, Svetlana lets out a huge belch that echoes off the walls, loud enough to make a German bartender proud. Then she resumes her tongue assault like nothing happened. Religious.

It's rare moments of clarity like this that restore my faith in humanity. They give me something to believe in. My special purpose. Surely binge-drinking threesomes are what God intended for my life.

-   -   -

The girls are satiated and all smiles, but I'm still too drunk to finish. My nuts are as polluted as two cocktail olives; if I come inside her she'll give birth to a hairy keg. I order up room service breakfast, and then we hit the shower to get the oil off. Lathering each other, it's an erotic group hug of slippery flesh. Things heat up again. The girls kneel down and give a competitive double hummer to see who gets the facial. Back and forth. Back and forth. It's a great visual. In the end Alek cheats. I'm not sure if it was her flawless technique or her slutty shameless hunger, but she hogged her last turn till she won the contest. So to be a good sport, I splash both their faces with a gallon of silly string.

I step out as they do the handheld shower nozzle soap show, washing and fingering each other. Always a crowd pleaser. While I'm brushing my teeth, it's pee pee time for the girls. If you've never seen it, it's a mild turn on to watch. Svetlana squats wide on the toilet and wizzes, then afterward chit chats using the bidet, washing and stroking herself. As for Aleksandra, that gorgeous girl men drool over strutting in her high heels and sophisticated outfits, she squats like a catcher over the drain in the corner of the shower. I peek in the mirror as she pees, washes, and then quietly fingers herself, her eyes closed, her head tilted back in the warm water cascading down.

Svetlana does the come here with the index finger. Standing above her on the toilet, she shares a sensual warm wet kiss, while I reach down and touch her stuff. Her pussy is fresh, bathed and shaved to a high gloss, accenting her swollen pink lips.

"Spread your legs for Daddy" Brett says, feeling a little feisty.

Her legs spread wide, I unload a nice long steady piss. A little splashing, but nothing too serious. (yuk, yuk). She looks up at me with a devilish smile, biting her lower lip. Reaching up with her tiny hand, she gently grabs my cock and steers the steady yellow stream up between her breasts, which cascades down her taut creamy belly between her thighs into the bowl. I raise an eyebrow and continue to blast away, a newbie porn fireman. She pulls me forward  for another sensual liplock. Hmmmm. Peeing on a babe I'm kissing at the same time. That's a first. I hope she remembers to shake. Not going to file this to the hard drive. I'd rather not change my perspective of walking around town lusting for women, to thinking *"there's a hot blonde…I'd like to pee on her head and take a dump in her panties drawer."* We hop back in the shower.

Shower done, we all collapse on the bed in a heap. Svetlana starts digging through the party pack and finds the strap on, which she's never seen before. Alek screams with laughter. She grabs it from her and saddles up behind Svetlana doggie style and slides it in.

Grins and giggles go round. Room service knocks announcing breakfast, which to me announces another hot young *dyev* soon to be in my room. The devious mind plots. I tell the girls don't stop.

Service girl enters the room, and almost drops the tray looking at the girls. Ahh, its Danilova. I've done her on two previous trips. A real cutie with a killer rack. All innocence and dimples, the girl next door type who never lives next door. She's a petite nubile with Gibraltar-like cheek bones, a tiny sunburn nose, cheeks covered in a pasture of red freckles, and lips that provide great attention to customer service.

Standing as always in a wet towel, I sign the bill with a huge tip, which she admires. She hands me the tray, and then rips off the towel, her hands doing a playful stroking. Little tiny kisses paint my cheeks, then for some reason she starts speaking. I immediately put a finger to her lips and push down on the top of her head. She kneels. In a slow tease she massages me, big wide eyes focused on the package. I feel her hot breath on the mushroom tip. Her tongue trails up and down the entire length of the shaft, with the head getting the softest sweet kisses and nibbles.

Looking up at me with innocent doe eyes, she purses her lips and starts bobbing and slurping, a hand gently cupping the balls while I casually eat breakfast from the tray watching ESPN. With such an expert touch, I can tell she's had lots of practice teasing and sucking a cock, really developing a passion for her position in the hotel industry. She moans and whimpers sucking it deeper, while stroking herself underneath her skirt with sticky fingers. After a few minutes, she asks if she can watch the girls. I slap her cheek with my cock, lift her up, and put the tray on the table.

It's quite a voyeur moment. Strap on removed, Svetlana is going down on Alek with a hyperactive tongue, bobbing her head wildly like a Woodpecker drunk on wild berries. I get behind Danilova at the edge of the bed, gently unzip and slide her mini-skirt to her ankles, admiring her frilly panties tight up the crack of her solid ass. She reaches behind her and pulls them out, slowly enough that as they reach a few inches from the crack, I can easily make out tiny little blonde hairs leading down to her bald moist pink mound.

Brett's kryptonite. Instant hard-on.

She bends over the edge of the bed, while I slide the dental floss panties over and guide it in. Her pussy is tight. Virgin tight. Damn is she wet. She releases an oooooffff moan and pained squeal, and pushes back against me hard. Then I perform the standard reach around with  one hand and pinch a nipple, while stroking the protruding clit with the other. Meeting all my strokes, she leans forward over the bed and starts kissing the moaning Alek. I try to take it slow, but sexy little Danilova is way too excited and comes in minutes, her hair splayed over her face. The room smells like a Chinatown fish market in a heat wave. Svetlana's face is buried nose deep in Aleksandra's pussy; she chokes on some juices and lets out another huge belch that echoes off the walls. WTF.

Danilova squirms and bounces in place, and pulls me out. Turning to face me, she locks lips with a furious passion, with both her hands pumping on my rod. She starts dancing in place crossing her thighs, and announces she has to leave or she's going to get in trouble. She yanks up her panties and skirt, grabs the bill and skips to the front door. She turns and opens the door and blows me a kiss. The bouncing light on the ceiling fan catches her body every half second, showing juices running down the inside of her smooth thighs. I love the little spontaneous teases. The girls downstairs will be all over her claims of innocence, and jealously dig for the dirty details.

"Danilova!" walking towards her.

"Da! Sorry…thanks so much Beast."

"Danilova!" "

What?' with a little confused whimper as she backs out the door into the hallway, a little girly girl scared.

"You were 3 minutes late delivering breakfast," and then I slam the door. I wait five seconds and open it. She standing there hands on hips, grinning ear to ear.

"I miss joo too much, Brett." She hops forward and kisses me and high heels it down the hallway. I watch her ass sway with a dirty old man's grin. As she waits at the elevator, even the plants lean in to get a whiff of her oozing panties.

Back inside, the girls have finished the 69 party and are begging for action, giving me the come here finger. With dirty grins paint their faces, I'm forced to comply, and lie on my back. Alek saddles up on top of the cock, while Svetlana sits on my mouth facing Alek. She leans forward and sucks on Alek's nipples and makes her way up to the lips. Alek is grunting hard and pounding me like the pornstar she is. Svetlana hops off my face, and out of the corner of my eye, I see her reach for the strap on and lube. This could be interesting. She straps it on, slicks it up, and then saddles up back on top of the bed behind Alek. Giddy up, kitty.

A long curious pause follows, while I anxiously stare into Aleksandra's eyes for the entry reaction. They squint and then bulge and then squint, and then I hear an ooooOOOOFFFFF. Svetlana is officially a Hershey bandit. She pumps her ferociously, while slapping her ass hard. Alek becomes a wild cat, her face drenched with sweat, humping me and then thrusting back against the strap on, a crazed nympho in an exotic DP session. Not three minutes later she screams and collapses onto my chest, gasping for air in ecstasy. I reach up and high five the giggling Svetlana. Brett hits the save button, and logs this delicious moment of depravity deep into the archives.

Alek's breathing gets fainter, collapsed on top of me in a powerful and noisy climax. I shake her for being lazy, and dare to her to make me cum. "*Yescho?*"(more) she asks. I put my finger on her lips. She pops off the chest. I throw down two pillows on the floor for their knees, while I sit on the edge of the bed. I love the look of two subservient babes in the double hummer position. This round proves to be much easier to reach the finale. Svetlana wins, much to Alek's jealousy. Only instead of a blast, I've run out of vanilla shake. All that happens is a little white flag comes out that says "Squirt "on it.

T he girls and I devour breakfast. They start making plans for shopping, lunch at some café, more sex, more meals and shopping, more sex, and staying the whole day. I inform them I have a busy schedule and it's time to dress. Nice try girls. What do I look like, a nice guy or something? Geez.

Time to kick them out and hit the gym hard. I need to sweat out gallons of liquor in my veins. I hand them each a healthy parting gift, and walk them out the door into the hallway wearing the towel. Svetlana sucks face and starts down the carpet. The night has taken its toll. She's mildly wobbly in her heels, hair messed up, looking like she just finished an amateur pornstar audition.

Alek hugs me a bit too long for comfort. Damn near five seconds.

"Next time joo in town, Brett, I stay vith joo all week. I do anything joo vant; I make joo happy man," says Alek.

Damn it, girl. She's falling hard again.

"Why would I do that? I already get what I want from you. Look baby, I can only handle you in small doses. You're too sexy. I'm too young to have a heart attack." Lies go down best coated with honey.

"Always the tough guy. I get vot I vant too. Maybe I vant a little more. Ok. Joo think about it."

She pushes me against the door and smothers me one last kiss.

Slow. Sensual. Like old lovers.

Ouch. I'm going to remember this one. She's something special. A girl who could really do some damage to my heart, if I wasn't such an insane hammered adrenaline junkie without a soul.

-   -   -

With Svetlana tapping a high heel waiting at the elevator, Alek goes to her, working that miracle ass down the hallway in that damn sexy strut of hers. I never get tired of watching her walk. I could make a whole voyeur afternoon of it. Set up bleachers, grab a cooler and popcorn and make her slither up and down the carpet back and forth, while I scratch my nuts and fart Smoke on the Water. What the hell. I'll walk the girls down to the street. Why miss out on a chance to piss people off with a quality Walk of Shame with two Penthouse pets. Give the audience what they want. I whistle and tell them to wait while I dress.

Brett puts on the incredulously bored look, strutting through the hotel lobby with two gorgeous statuesque models, one hand wrapped around the waist, the other cupping my butt. Another day at the office. While a horse drawn chariot galloping across a lowered drawbridge seems more appropriate, the show is still offensive enough to make the male guests grin ear-to-ear with bulging eyes and tent pants, and the beefy wenches launch into fits of elephantine rage.

As we step outside, the old coot is holding court with his gaggle of pigeons and a stray young dyev, from his hallowed perch on the park bench. His eyes are perpetually scanning the horizon for his stately ship to come in. Puffing on a mahogany Brigham Classic tobacco pipe beneath his tweed pancake hat, he's got the girl laughing away, while feeding his pigeons some seed. Out of the corner of his eye he sees Brett with the hotties. His eyes go wide, and then squint, and then wide again. He abruptly sits up ramrod straight, his weathered hand gripping the turquoise knob of his cane tightly. He waves for me to bring the girls over. Hmmm. A little feisty today. Hope old Scrappy has a fresh pair of depends on. His girl's eyes connect with us, and she walks away back towards the hotel.

As we walk over, he has a big huge grin that slowly shrinks with each step closer. Reaching him, he actually looks dejected, and starts methodically re-loading tobacco into his trusty pipe.

"Why the sad face Gramps, that time of the month?" Brett asks, trying to cheer him up.

His eyes go back and forth inspecting the girls' faces, and then he looks away at the morning sun peeking through the glass towers.

"No games, my friend. Why did you want to meet the girls if you are just going to turn away? You're not one of them there Trans-testicles, are you?" showing the utmost respect for the elderly.

The silence is broken by the old man smacking his fleshy lips. He looks back at the girls sheepishly, and heaves a sigh.

"For a moment, I thought one of them may be a long lost friend," while thumbing that shiny medallion around his neck at a maniacal pace. He starts to wave us off, then pauses and takes a deep breath.

"We won't bite, vat is it you vant sir?" Svetlana asks.

"It's a long story." He takes the medallion off his neck and opens it. Nestled inside is a faded pic of a beautiful, classy Russian blonde.

"By chance has either of you ladies seen this woman? She would be five or so years older than this photo."

The girls lean forward and look closely, speaking in rapid Russian to each other. The old guy eyes their reaction keenly. His massive eyebrows dance in anticipation, a bright sparkle in his wet hazel eyes that could be mistaken for tears.

"Nyet, I'm sorry sir. But if vee do, who's looking for her?"

"Broderick Chesterfield III " he beams with pride. "Just tell her to meet me here at this hotel. She'll remember it."

"Nice to meet joo sir. Brett, we get cab now."

We walk holding hands over to the taxi stand.

Alek gives me a long final hug, her body infinitely warm and sweet smelling.

"Brett, joo remember vott I asked you, yes?"

"I'll think about it Alek. It was nice to see me again. You to Svetlana." I kiss them both as deep and obscene as possible in front of the valet guy. The cab pulls up and I put Alek's hands on the door, stand behind her ass and pump it doggie style for 5 seconds like a beast and pretend to finish, moaning horribly. I give the girls cab fare and see them off.

The look on the valet guy's face was priceless.

Walking back to the hotel, I glance over at the fiery old coot. He's still opening and closing the medallion obsessively.

"There's something you're not telling me pops" I yell out.

He glances with his eyes glazed over, like he's not all there, and returns his stare at the medallion.

"Maybe later, OK? Be careful young man," I say to him, turning to the hotel.

"I hope you find what you're looking for son. You're a lot further from it today than you were yesterday" he says with a tip of his Gatsy cap, and a wheezing old geezer cackle, launching into a phlegmy pipe cough that has the pigeons ducking for cover.

It's workout and re-group time. It's a big night tonight. Viktor and I will be roadhouse slumming at the infamous Hungry Duck. It promises to be a fine evening of debauchery at the sleaziest club in all of Moscow.

Mmmmm. Alek. What a slice of sensual, primitive lust. It's an act of rare kindness choosing not to string her along. Only with my cynical porn shields can I rescue myself from not falling for her and destroying my life. She wants to own me, to save me, wants me to save her. It's tough, but it's the smart move to push her away. Why go through with a stormy relationship that would age me ten years in a month? It would affect my work, my health, my wallet, not to mention finding the time to pee on Svetlana's tits again. Next!

The infamous Ivan the Great Bell Tower from inside the Kremlin Walls. Built by Marco Bon Fryazin in 1505, replacing an old stone church from 1329. That's the Assumption Chapel in the background, They comprise Russia's original ritual center where grand princes were proclaimed, Czars were enthroned and emperors were crowned; the resting place of the heads of the Russian church of the 14th-17th centuries. The Ivan the Great Bell tower served as the Kremlin's main watchtower, as the top terrace allows a 30 kilometer view of surrounding Moscow turf. The bell tower is 81 meters high, the walls of the first tier are 5 meters thick, and those of the second are 2.5 meters thick. In 1812 Napoleon's troops placed explosives at the base of the bell tower, but it withstood the blast. The bells of the tower fell silent in 1918 and rang once again at Easter in 1992. There are 21 bells cast in the 16th century in the galleries of the tiers. The largest of them, the Assumption Bell, which weighs 70 metric tons.

17.

THE CALM BEFORE THE STORM

Boulevard Ring Park

Back to the room, I down two liters of ice water for recovery. I actually feel pretty good as I'm still quazi-ripped and may skate past the hangover stage. It will be the usual routine this morning; a big gym workout to sweat a gallon of the alcohol, and then back to the room for more water, brunch and a 20 min. powernap. Feeling like a cerebral Tarzan, I daytrade options and futures for an hour, make a few business calls to check pending deals and catch up with old clients. Come noon, it's time to hit the streets.

I skipped the treadmill today as I need to put in some significant mileage, as I'm running in a marathon relay in a few days. I cab it over to **Boulevard Ring Park**, which circles the heart of the city; a nice paved park with walkways, trees and grass. It's an 8 km loop, similar to Central Park but better for running, as the course doesn't contain NYC finest begging and swinging knives and bats. I've hooked up often here with rollerbladers and runners and wide-eyed strollers. There must be a fashion trade show in town, because today it's packed with models in skin tight designer everything. I do two loops totaling 16km. I slowed my pace at one point, and ran with two scorchers for a mile, and hit the record button on my armband iPOD to memorize their numbers. Dates and bonks scheduled, mileage put in, it's back to the hotel for lunch and a hair of the dog Bloody Mary.

18.
THE MOUTH – THE RETURN OF IVANA SUCKIT

Moscow's New International Business Center complex

- - -

Back to the room for a quick shower, lunch, and it's time to attack the room bar. A few hours go by in hurry, and so does a six, three Bloody Marys and an embarrassing large number of shots. I watched the same cycled series of highlights on ESPN five times, and get hammered enough that I swore the last two were live. Although I'm very anxious to hit it hard tonight with Viktor, once the buzz kicks in, there's only one thing I can think of. THE MOUTH. (the chick from the lunch café yesterday).

With about two hours to kill before Viktor arrives, I've got enough time to knock off a quick one. I ring up The Mouth on her cell. To no surprise, she answers in half a ring.

"So, did you keep that thing warm for me?"

"Da! Eetz steaming, baby. Joo vant come over for dat taste?

"Only if you answer the door naked." I hear giggling and hang up before she answers. I hate it when they play hard to get.

Her apartment address is a ten minute walk; just a few city blocks, and down a series of side streets. Nothing too scary, if I recall the area correctly. In a flash, Brett throws on his best Saturday evening hummer attire, pops a Viagra and is out the door in seconds flat. Like a stealthy lion sprinting for the kill.

No emotion. Pure instinct.

Whipping past the front desk and the hottie lollipop brigade, he speed walks out the front door.

The old man stands from his VIP bench, his James Smith & Sons mahogany umbrella gripped tight in his right hand. Leaning against a lamp post in his charcoal gray pinstriped suit, he belts out his two cents while nodding with paternal condescension;

"I wish I had the answer for you."

"What answer is that, oh Great One?"

"Come now. I've been where you are in life, my boy. It's written all over your face. You're looking for something, but you're in way too much of a hurry to find it."

"I think I can find it tonight, Gramps. I've got directions. Even shitfaced I can read my own handwriting."

"Hah! Be careful son. Patience comes to those who wait."

"Looks like you've been a bit too patient. Cheer-e-ohh, my good lad. Great to see me again."

-   -   -

Whipping down the street for three blocks, I cruise into the Mom and Pop newsstand again for a bottle of Vodka and a chaser Heineken 12-pack. The panty-dropping fuel procured, I'm out of the store in a flash. As I leave, I hold open the door for a set of legs in a skimpy peach miniskirt that are impossibly long, sexy, and defined. Watching her prance by, as I exit my shirt catches the corner of door, spinning me around in a wicked 360, nearly launching the booze and causing a hideous face plant into the cement steps. Fortunately Brett's ninja-like agility makes another heroic save. A taxi driver honks, dreaming of owning this uncanny alcoholic talent.

Drawn like a magnet, I peek in for the token voyeur moment. Mmmm. Damn I love this city! Eyeing her stuff up and down like a drooling teenager in a lab jacket with the trusty clipboard, I check out her package. We've got luscious athletic thighs (check!), sexy contoured calves, a studded ankle bracelet above stripper high heels; all attached to an exquisitely chiseled body. She wears a half-unbuttoned blouse with a see-thru lace bra underneath. Nipples at attention. There's a delicious ass branded with the tramp stamp, frantic brunette hair that looks like it got caught in a ceiling fan, and a tiny diamond stud in her nose. The helmet is provocatively slutty, with heavy aqua eye shadow above a pearl white necklace.

Hummpphh, Brett mumbles while scratching his nuts. A certified party chick looking for some action. It's a shame, too. I'm running on a tight blowjob schedule, so I'll have to pass. The Viktor ETA to prime trim hunting is down to 75 minutes.

- - -

Turning to resume the speed walk down the sidewalk, I go ten feet and there's an abandoned baby carriage with a little brat in it. No Mom in sight. WTF! Always the debonair gentleman, Brett parks it until someone re-claims the little rug rat. Costing $800+, upscale baby carriages are a commodity for the Moscow rich, which could mean the Mom's possibly model material. I consider pawning the thing for a quick $100 and practicing my rugby dropkick, but settle for a liquor pit stop.

Brett cracks a Heineken, which sprays the kid a bit, (oops), and resumes the day's blistering drinking pace. Four minutes later, bottle one is gone. *Kachingg*. I crack another, toast myself, and tilt it back. After ripping a healthy series of baritone German belches, those same sleek gazelle legs come out of the store with a huge Stolichnaya Vodka bottle in tow.

She approaches me like a magnet. It can't be for my breath. Her walk is sensual and fluid, never permitting my eyes to waver. This is one sensual *dyev* who's got flirting down to a science. Almost theatrical. It's a cultivated appearance,  refined through years of seducing men. Men are her pawns to be toyed with and exploited for amusement or rent. Brett looks on coolly disinterested, a seasoned Casanova immune to her powers.

"Ex-squeeze me honey, can you help?" I ask, picturing her naked and chained to a leaking '68 Vette tranny in my garage.

"It seems this little angel's Mom is missing. I must say, she's one of the most beautiful babies I've ever seen," laying it on thick. I reach down and wipe the beer drops off the kid's cheeks. "Poor thing's been crying too. Here sweetie, let me get that."

"Da, you're either too kind, or drunk" in a high girly voice, like a soft melody.

Her body language is warm and feminine. The face is inviting and yet reserved, with high cheekbones, and a thin upturned nose resting delicately above full lips. In the store, the eyes were hidden. Up close, I find them an intense ice blue; slanted, large blue beacons like I've never seen on a woman. She slides over next to me and straps the vodka bottle in the seat next to the baby!

Like any concerned citizen with paternal instincts, as she leans forward towards the little dropkick, I drop down and pretend to tie my shoes for a quick upskirt of the goods. What's this? A puffy pink smile peeking out. No panties! Yes! (*bow chika chika bow bow*).

Despite her being 32ish, she has a Ms. Fitness Pageant body, with a sexy round workout butt pressing tightly against her miniskirt, inching the hem higher as she moves. Her face is that classic been around the block but still goddamn beautiful look.

Interesting.
A *dyevushka Cougar*.

While certainly not record book material, it would make a nice aged trophy for the mantle; maybe use it as a bookend. There's something else about her, though. The way she moves. Sensual. An air of dominance and sexual confidence. Oh ohh…the damn Viagra is starting to kick in big time. Down boy.

"You're not old enough to be her Mom. Do you know whose precious daughter she is," reaching nauseating levels of charm and BS, while picturing her crouched on dirty knees wiping my handiwork off her puffy lips with the back of her hand.

"Do I have to pay you for deez things you say?" twirling her hair while crossing one foot in front of the other with a demure smile.

The unmistakable CFM pose.

"Nice set of wheels you've got there. Were you born with them, or did you have to earn them?"

"Ha! All carriages come with da wheels. So, are joo bee-zee tonight?" she asks, as I peek at her hooha heaven, deliciously firm and barely concealed by her Victoria Secret bra.

"I'm curious. You have that face like you're looking for something, (trying the old man's line). Do I sense built up *Sexual Energy* that needs satisfying, Mom?" while moving closer in her space. Standing eye to eye. Feeling her ooze body heat.

"Mmmm; a mind reader too" while tonguing her lips.

"So tell me stranger, are joo in da *Sexual Energy* beeziness?"

"The CEO baby. Listen. I'm in a hurry right now. Give me your cell and I'll see if my secretary can find time to fill you in."

"*Nyet.* I not interested in jour secretary. When JOO vant to fill me in, give me call," she says, one hand gently around my waist, the other softly resting around the nape of my neck. She gives me the tiniest of kisses, with half closed slutty eyes inches from mine.

"Nice to meet joo, well, um both of joo. I should leave as well. I'm not sure da little one is old enough to see deez." She points to my tent pole pants. Shit!

Not bad for an old bird. I mean in this town, 32ish is a friggin'dinosaur. She's a seriously sexy one, though. What the hell, I'll be a good sport about it. Even grannies need loving too. I get her digits, and save her name in the *mobilniki* as Nympho MILF.

I rarely ask for girls' names anymore.

What's the point?

Hurrying down the sidewalk, it's time to move off Tversaka Avenue before some crusty old linebacker sized hens hunting tourist sausage get the wrong idea. Using the Heineken as a crotch cover, I hang a left down the first side street. Switching gears immediately, I negotiate the terrain like a bombed, navy seal. With eyes at once passive and alert, I shuffle along in a disguised local's casual walk, crisscrossing sides to bypass the drunks weaving, skinheads, junkies, revolutionaries, mad poets, packs of wild dogs, and assorted wastes of oxygen and cultural debris.

The biggest thorn is the huddled street punks with contorted faces and thick necks bulging with veins, looking in frustration for ways to prove their manhood. Fortunately they're being mauled by a gaggle of bored flathead cops, extracting bribes and swinging truncheons at random idiots for sport. One unlucky thug lies unconscious in a mangled heap, his features grotesque and twisted out of shape. His eyes are half open and head slumped. A steady narrow stream of blood mingles with a puddle of filthy street slime, forming swirling circles in the intermittent light of the street lamps.

With the moon shrouded in cloud cover, the streets are dark and ominous; the lone tree chokes on low-grade diesel exhaust and burning tires. Moscow's angry night weather is moving in. The cold wind is piercing and steady; it's sound a low whistle. Barely visible under dim cheap neon bulbs, half the storefronts are boarded up vacant shells, autographed with nazi logos, and artist renderings of public figures decorated with knives and bullet holes. A scant few blocks from the main drag is the bleak generation left behind; the wretched Moscow boom a heroic disappointment to a numb, lubricated society. No hopes. No dreams of prosperity. It's the survival of the un-fittest.

Brett hurdles down the sidewalk over a sleeping 3-legged dog with four saggy nipples, lime-green puddles of urine and vomit, and rusted machinery. While I gag for anything resembling oxygen, a faint scream of metal on metal looms in the distance and stops. The sound is brief. Its echo lingering a tad longer. A bird flutters away in a mad urgency. The pigeon's path rises from the belly of dark alleys, arching higher and lower avoiding the drooping electrical wires.

The metallic sound returns, and car alarms go off in rolling waves.

A massive construction truck plunders down the avenue and slowly rolls by, shredding the decayed street with its tonnage, churning mud and asphalt in every direction. With catlike reactions, Brett bobs and weaves like a kickoff returner in a cold sprint. He finishes with a spike of his dead Heineken into a dumpster, holding a perfect frozen Heisman statue pose finish.

BRETT TATE — 175

Lying flat out on the sidewalk, a hammered Brit smelling like rotting flesh slurs out in his best John Madden voice; "there'sssh a fumble on the play, its Ohio Sshtate's ball on UCLA sshix yard line! He chokessh again!", and then launches into a long wheezing laugh indicating a lifetime of cheap tobacco.

Witty stuff. Excellent timing and delivery. He's clutching the Ted Kaczynski survival guide *"How to Live on Vodka, Beef Jerky and Puke...repeat."* The Brit's face shares a heritage with a junkyard butt-sniffing mutt. It's a hard-earned red moonshine mug dotted with a hairy mole that looks like a rat's been gnawing on it. His beard looks like a white sneeze, the teeth are jagged and out of alignment, having opened quarts at Jiffy Quick Lube for half a decade. The hair impossibly thick. It's a rule. Going bald? Just quit your job, move into a shopping cart and chug liters of moonshine. Done.

Brett considers complimenting the Brit's humor, right up to the part when he flips me off and tries to trip me as I walk past, so I offer up some charity.

"You look at bit hungry, snaggletooth. Wanna gnaw on my dingleberries, or should I take a dump on your head?"

"Wot? Wot dyoo say? C'mere ya cunt."

Without hesitation, I spin, line up and give him a meaty soccer style kick in the ass.

"Beckham shoots...GGOOAAAALLLLLLL!!"

"How 'bout a fookin' tip, ya bassshtard!"

"Here's your tip, Einstein. *Be careful young man.*" Geez. If I had the time, I'd drag him behind a 4X4 through a cactus patch.

Finding the Mouth's crib is no easy task. The apartment buildings are a haphazard row of identical granite and concrete slabs of exhausted grays, despairing browns and peeling pastel flakes, battling time and wearing the tattoos of retro graffiti. Buildings squatting linearly in communist conformity, my attempts to identify apartments let alone building numbers is a comedy act for sober men. Despite the obstacles, Brett loves all of this. Even when the girl is a sure thing, the thrill of the chase on foreign turf is so money. The hairs on your neck rise. The heart races. There's just nothing like the bizarre Wild West feeling of danger during new coochie conquests.

- - -

It's a long way from the life I left behind. Most of my friends are either married or dead, and I can't tell the difference. Their wild evenings consist of slouching in the beer stained rocker watching Friends reruns through squinting eyes, pretending to be asleep while the beefy self-centered, neurotic wife (on heavy meds) screeches at them for ignoring her latest imaginary crisis. Romance consists of buying feed for her trough, and being treated like an emotional tampon and walking ATM machine. For the mere price of half their assets, these guys' lives are spent in a fashion quite similar to wandering around on the grounds of an insane asylum and listening to the rambling nonsense. For some reason, a 200 pound unemployed shrieking monster swinging a rolling pin at my head for not taking out the trash lacks a certain appeal.

- - -

W hipping up and down a few blocks in a vodka haze, I get lost, and wind up looping around, only to go down the same street twice like a short bus dork. Between the buzz and the coochie anticipation, the feet are actually hovering above the pavement. By pure accident, I stumble into what appears to be her apartment. Good thing. One block the wrong way is a really bad area.

A quick call to The Mouth verifies my luck. She opens the door butt naked as requested, wearing nothing but a big huge smile, thigh high

lace stockings and heels. In the living room I hear Trent Reznor of Nine Inch Nails singing, *"I want to fuck you like an animal. I want to feel you from the inside."* I strut in looking bored. My BJ threads are styling. My stiff-o-meter is pinned.

My hair is perfect.

She takes my hand and walks me to the kitchen, puts the booze in the fridge, and hands me a Heineken. No eye contact. No speaking. She leers at my crotch, and then walks me to the couch, her heels clicking on the faded brownish yellow terra-cotta tiles as she crosses the room. I thought maybe we could chat about the potential arbitrage between oil futures contracts vs. leap call options in Russia's Lukoil stock, and the unintended consequences of Yeltsin selling the country to his buddies for a song. She thought not. She thought she should bow down and suck me like a human vacuum cleaner.

Without even a kiss, she grabs a pillow from the couch, gets down on her knees and I hear the familiar zzzzziiiiiipppp sound. The girl is a sexual control freak in a hurry. What am I, just a piece of meat? Can't you hold me and drone on and on about your imaginary problems? Friends re-runs start in ten minutes…do you mind?

My throbbing weapon pops out pointing ram-rod straight, like a walking Viagra ad. She raises a curious eyebrow above her librarian glasses, and a dirty smile paints her lips. Whispering something in Russian, she sucks on a finger and reaches down and starts fingering her steaming pussy, while staring me in the eye with heavy eyelids above her gorgeous baby blues. Her right hand curls around my shaft; her grip light and sensual. Admiring her seduction trance, I take a cold Heineken and press it against my sweaty forehead.
Damn.
Getting a Blowjob is hard work.
Pray for me Oprah.

She rips the pants down to the ankles, and slowly peels my brand new blue boxers lower, while licking her massive wet lips. My rod admires them juicy Michelin sized lips with great anticipation, like a suicidal goldfish approaching a starving suckerfish. As she leans in to tease, I notice a long piece of boxer blue fur on the tip of my dick. It disappears in a hurry, as The Mouth devours me. By instinct, as she passes the halfway point, I hit the stopwatch. The official hummer time is four minutes and five seconds after arriving. I can almost hear Viktor saying "Nice try, comrade. I not born yesterday. Only first hummer after airport counts, Brett!"

Through the paper thin walls, I hear underground death metal, and two high-pitched, drunken giggles from girls shuffling around in the next apartment. Reaching down, I roll The Mouth's budding puffy nipples between my fingers, while drooling over her teeming erect funbags pointing north, the kind only found on fresh, untarnished youth. Despite the lack of a flat head and handlebars ears, her oral sluttiness is quite the view. I watch her performance in third person; like a video director.

You can't help but be in awe when you hook up with a young girl who's so experienced. To say she gives great head would be the understatement of the year. There's oral sex, and then there's a porn star blowjob. She gives the latter. Her technique is perfect. Deep throat, heavy lidded eyes locked on mine, the occasional licks up the vein on the backside, a slow building pace and steady rhythm with the twisty hand twirling combined with slippery turbo suction that has my toes curling in seconds.

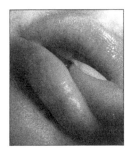

She was born with the perfect lips and mouth. I raise a Heineken and toast the BJ Gods for her talent. It's all Mouth, all the time. She is in complete control from second one, and could finish me off anytime she wanted. After just five minutes into it, it was already time for me to make a decision on returning the favor and then drilling her, or painting her face.

I decide to slow her down by picking her up and French kissing her for a few seconds. She makes out briefly, and pushes me away and gets back on her knees, sucking even deeper. She's on a cream mission. Placing my palm on the back of her head, I ball up her beautiful long whitish blonde hair in my fist and shove her head inward. Feeling something in between my front teeth, I dig my finger in and pull out the blue thread.

The Mouth. A Virtual Sucking Machine.

Within minutes I get the sucked in G-force cheeks, the body gets tense with electric sensations, my hair starts whipping in my face, angels start singing, and just when I'm standing on my tippytoes about to explode, the front door flies wide open, and in comes Nympho MILF pushing the baby carriage! **She's her Mom!**

She looks at the Mouth on her knees, looks at me, looks back at The Mouth and asks; "I thought you had homework to do?"

"I do it later. I busy right now." Slurp. Grin. Lick.

"I can see that."

The carriage gets parked in the foyer, and her purse is thrown down on the kitchen table with a humpffff. She walks up to me and stands eye to eye. Arms on her hips. A high heel speed tapping madly. I stand there in disbelief. I'm either getting slapped, or have hit the porno jackpot. The silence is deafening.

Despite Mom lecturing her, The Mouth is a focused oral vacuum cleaner. She never stops inhaling my cock for a second. She's sucking and swirling her tongue back and forth, licking and looking up at me with irresistible teenage dimples and a naughty spark in her eye. This is somehow just a high school game to her, a way to show up her Mom.

Brett enjoys the show. He's happy to meet such a nice healthy family, in touch with their unique emotional wants and needs, and getting along nicely despite jealousy issues.

"Joo really are da CEO of da Sexual Energy beeziness. I see you've met my daughter," smiling demurely, yet pissed.
"We go way back."
"Da! To da back of her throat."

With a dismissive wave, the MILF walks past my BJ Queen into the kitchen. She pulls out a Vodka bottle from the freezer, and slams it in on the dinner table. She really is jealous. Her daughter beat her old ass to the gringo cock. She pours several tall shots of vodka and coolly strolls back over and hands me one. She winks. We click glasses and chug.

"Forgive me. My daughter so horny, she forgets her manners," looking over in condescending disapproval.

Walking tall in her slippery seductive way, she saunters across the faded tile floor and plants herself on the couch. Her smooth bronzed legs slung up onto the pillows, stilettos unsheathed, wearing a body-hugging skirt with the hemline just inches below the waist. She whispers to herself with distant eyes. Taking a heel off and gently massaging a foot, she eyes The Mouth doing her magic with a cynical smirk and winks at me. Replacing the shoe, she makes sure to give me a full view of her panty-less cookie, before popping up and standing next to her daughter.

19.
POCAHOTASS AND THE MILF DILF BJ CONTEST

Nympho MILF puts her shot glass down. Snagging a pillow, she drops it on the floor next to my feet. She leans forward. Pulling my face to hers, she gives me a toe curling sensual kiss, hungrily sucking on my tongue and probing my lips while running her fingers around the nape of my neck. The Mouth keeps working her magic, sensing she's about to lose her prize.

"Aren't joo going to offer me some of dat deek?"

"Come on, Mom. I here first," giggling and slapping my cock against her flush cheek. Crazy. Sexy. Hypnotic.

Nympho MILF locks eyes with me, and slowly unzips her miniskirt from behind, peeling it off while licking her lips. She kicks it off smooth like an ex-dancer, in all her naked glory.
"*I see you…,*" says the Johnson, the Master of the Obvious.

Ouch. What a slamming tight package! Her top gets ripped off and lands in the whore clothes pile. Da Cougar is bringing it! Her cut body is perfect – seductive - beautifully nude. The rack is majestic artistry. Her plastic surgeon's place in history is alongside Michelangelo. She's even got six-pack abs; the kind you want to eat a greasy burger and fries off of before curling up in her belly button snoring and drooling bubbles.

She kneels down butt naked on the pillow, next to her naked daughter. I dab my eyes in touching moments of maternal love like this. All is not lost. Yes. Hope is still alive. The future holds great promise. At least my future does. If I had a remote control for that damn baby carriage, I could wheel that thing over and take a family photo…steal the kid's huge Stoli bottle. The Mouth laughs at Mommy for being so horny. The MILF spanks her, and takes my stiff rod from The Mouth.

"Enuff. Move. Let me show joo how eetz done."

Naturally I'm curious how the MILF will hold up to the competition. The Mouth came out sucking strong in the pole position. For the MILF, foreplay is definitely out. Oh no. This oral SmackDown will be swift and decisive. While staring at me with those smoldering blue eyes, she parts her full lips and completely deep throats me, her nose firmly pressed against my stomach. Dohhh! So older woman really can serve a purpose in life!

The Mouth makes a pouty face, unimpressed.

"Whatever," she says, and after a couple deep throat pumps yanks the sausage out of her Mom's mouth with a popping sound, and swallows it deep.

The Great Russian suck-off begins. I close my eyes in an intoxicating sexual daze, hearing a steady rhythm of heavy breathing and rapid wet slurping, like sucking noodles through a straw from a deep stone dish. Fortunately, as the nympho scene unfolded, I managed to regroup and regain my whiskey dick  - Viagra stamina. I raise my Heineken and toast myself. Time check. *T minus 58 minutes to meet Viktor.*

As the two of them battle back and forth, I glance back in the doorway and see the baby in the carriage. Facing me. Eye to eye. A possible wink. The rug rat has put her arm around the vodka bottle strapped in the seat next to her, like it's her brother. She's making her own slurping noises working her pacifier. Acting a little cocky about her no handed control. Watching her destiny.

A rather uncomfortable sight.

Tracking sex trophies for the mantle is important business to a Professional Bachelor. I'm tempted to ask the Mouth if she is her kid, making it three generations, but seeing as my dick is in the back of her throat, the timing seemed off. Her bobbing and concentration is intense. Why mess with a master hard at work? Right about now, I can't help but notice there's some ungodly odor seeping into the room.

"Good God. What the hell is that horrible smell?"

"Dat's Rasputin. He good dog, but he sick for month now. He in next room sleeping."

"Sick?! He smells like a Yankee's shitter in an August heat wave."

MILF gets up to check on him, but first gently runs her fingers through The Mouth's hair, and kisses her on the top of her head. Not maternally. A bit too affection. Interesting. She leaves the room snapping that hot ass in her high heels, and comes back spraying air freshener.

"As long as he sleeps dere be no problem."

- - -

She casually walks past the Hoover on her knees to the kitchen table. Picking up the vodka chugging pace, this time she pours four rounds of tall double shots, which we throw back in a hurry. Damn. Yet another purpose for older women.

After five minutes of the double hummy, the time comes to accelerate my field research. The sexual deviancy possibilities of a MILF DILF combo are just too ripe not to pursue. My devil horns rise as the trumpets announce the debauchery shall begin, as written in Roman tablatures. I help the MILF up and sit her on the couch, and stack the Mouth on top of her lap, leaning back against her funbags with her legs spread. She presents me her hairless pussy and quivering firm ass cheeks. Still in the speed sex position with my pants around my ankles, I kneel down on a pillow with the red laser dot traveling up her thighs.

What a view…a vertical snapper sandwich! It's like one long pink smile! And I will indulge like Gandhi after a month long fast, and the people will rejoice. Rejoice I tell you. The teasing begins; my tongue tickles inches away from the honey holes, while fingernails gently glide up their thighs and stop inches away from the wet spots. Nipples get pinched and bitten, heaving racks get the saline squeeze test; I kiss the nape of their necks and work my way down. The girls are dripping and arching their hips begging for more. Back and forth I move, with hands and fingers stroking in so many directions; they must think I'm part Russian octopus. Brett accelerates the pace and pushes their buttons to the edge. The Mouth loses control and playfully grabs my hair and pushes my nose deep in between her tasty pink folds.

"Less passion, more aggression?" I ask with eyes blinking full of virgin innocence.

She nods. And so it begins.

- - -

As I take turns on their lean bodies, the pussies become shiny and glistening wet, until the pretty pink clits pop out from the meat flaps. I put on a snorkel, and lick the two coochies up and down, back and forth, inside and out, lick occasionally a little too low, while thumbing their clits and massaging the G-spot using the "come here" index finger motion. It's a patented technique, perfected in field tests  on four continents in twelve languages. Brett's been around. He does all the tricks. He has no shame. Girls like that about him.

Having a Pussy PHD, my research has found snappers are rarely identical, even in the same family. In this case, The Mouth has pink pubescent thin lips, and a shy hidden hood covering a teenie weenie Lolita clit. Nympho MILF has huge purplish meat flaps that she claps like flamenco castanets, and a swollen clit that almost makes her look hung. The Mouth has the faint airy scent of morning spring daises. The MILF is a hold-your-breath teary eyed swamp thing; if she was on all fours and raised her hind leg, she could melt candle wax in the apartment next door. Surprisingly, she brought a mound of hair to this party, clearly out of touch with the times. I mean really, honey. Do I look like a greens keeper doing a Toro mulcher commercial? Brett prefers a juicy smooth moneymaker without a ZZ Top awning.

By contrast, The Mouth is a baby-smooth pink cookie of lickable dreams. In a blind taste test, there would be no contest. One thing they both have in common, though. Their *pizdas* like to be licked, and are going to be drilled hard by Brett the Beast.

- - -

How they react when getting head varies as well. The Mouth is young and new to being devoured by a sexual deviant like me. She completely loses it. She bucks and thrusts her hips to match the finger fucking and licking. The MILF savors the feeling with a sensual coolness, having banged half the eastern bloc during her first marriage while da hubby was at work. Feeling them both getting close, I back off and tease them like the prick I am, enjoying the power and lust. This brings slaps. I like that.

I accelerate licking the pink tacos, and then back off again. They give slutty Russian commands and shove my head down. I like that even more. Finally, the Russian lickmaster takes over and goes for the finish. Bear with me, cruel world. My work is tedious, but my mission is noble.

The legs start uncontrollable shaking as the squeeze boxes tighten with a smooth creaminess; the air fills with two octaves of sex noises and grunts. The Mouth gives high pitched staccato ooo-ooOO—OOO!!! squeals, while Nympho MILF takes deep breaths and lets out old school throaty whore moans, like my Uncle does when he slices off a mean dump with the door open during halftime. As for me, I sound like a parched St. Bernard lapping away in the toilet, with a puddle of slobber and drool dribbling down my chest.

A slow dynamic crescendo builds in volume and intensity. The plants start swaying in rhythm, the baby smacks the carriage handlebars giggling, the dog starts barking, until the apartment walls shake and echo to the sounds of a simultaneous, multi-generational, cross-hemisphere Big O' Orchestra. I tilt the head back and beat my chest and launch the Tarzan yell. Geez. I bet my breath smells like I've been chewing on defensive end's dirty socks. I tilt back and chug the last half of the Heineken; make that dirty German socks, thank you.
T minus 46 minutes till Viktor.

"Hi vant cock NOW!," The Mouth demands as she flips over into doggie position, straddling her stuff above Mommy. With my pants at my ankles and the clock ticking fast, *Brett the Beast* stands up and starts his engine. There's no time for gentle soothing caresses and romantic hold me thoughts. The doggie style egg timer has been turned over, and I'm a porn star in a hurry.

Ramming. Slamming. Pumping that heart shaped ass hard and fast. Since it's doggie style, while doing her I put on a hat with floppy ears and lap at a dirty bowl of water on her back. The Mouth is pushing back towards me meeting every thrust, her pussy squeezing my prick as it slips in and out. This is good. This is real good.

The MILF has her own dirty thoughts, and slides a bit down the couch. Positioned underneath, her lips purse as she sucks on The Mouth's nipples, slowly tracing a line with her tongue from the left to right nipple, and licks down to the belly button. The Mouth moans uncontrollably and tilts her head back. Now were talking. MILF runs her fingers around the puffy areolas, and slides down off the couch at my feet. Above her head is the best view in the house. To be a good sport, I pull out and let her deepthroat me for a bit. As I resume pumping away and slapping the ass, MILF reaches up and parts the shaved pink folds, stroking the Mouth's clit. Brett coolly nods his head, an experienced leader in family counseling.

A bizarre noise catches my attention in the hallway. Rasputin the stink bomb is barking and causing havoc with that IQ of Five brain of his. Like a possessed quadruped, he's spinning in circles trying to bite his own tail, while blasting deep death farts that kill the flowers on the wallpaper. Judging by the doggie grin, he considers these to be generous pungent gifts to be shared amongst loved ones, and we should be thankful. The MILF counters with a few swift blasts of air freshener, but it's no match for these bombs. Despite the action packed lust in the living room, my attention is definitely waning; the beast horns go to half mast as the room is starts to fill with a vile, rank odor.

But there's still hope. Finally the moment I've been waiting for. While I'm pumping away like a demon just above her mouth, The MILF raises her head to just the right angle, and starts licking The Mouth's clit, tracing long strokes up and down the pinkness.

Nibbling, licking and sucking her daughter's labia and clit. The Mouth starts quivering and completely loses it, eyes closed, lost in her lengthy orgasm. In just thirty seconds, the oohs and aahs peak, signaling yet another screaming orgasm. This time she's so loud it brings some pounding on the walls from the jealous neighbors next door. Brett notes  the score on his mental chalkboard, and pulls out and smacks the MILF's cheekbone with his rod, letting her know it's her turn.

-   -   -

The MILF slides back halfway onto couch on her back, as the MOUTH changes positions. Facing me, she sits up on her knees, and positions her love box just over top the MILF's tongue in 69 position. I kneel down on my knees, and slide into the MILF's tuna taco, holding her ankles high in the air. She lets out a deep moan. Her fingers reach up and spreads The MOUTH's honeyhole, and she starts giving her soft flat tongue licks.

I raise my Heineken and toast the Gods of Testosterone.

Oh My. This is why they invented confession booths, although at my church when I close the door, the first thing the priest says is *do you want to go first?* The girls make quite the irresistible tag team; spicy, spunky and erotic. By virtue of my overwhelming charisma, it seems the girls have smoothed over any mother/daughter jealousy issues at the moment. We do this position for a few minutes, until the MILF decides she needs to accelerate the sleaze levels.

"Baby, joo vant poot jour deek in da ass? I think joo vant!"

"Yes Mam," not one to offend a senior citizen.

With her ankles pointing to the ceiling, she's at the perfect angle. It's like two deep dish beer holders with vertical handlebars. I must say, for an old bird of 30ish she's got just the right kind of hot athletic body; a toned gym rat aerobic body with supple athletic muscles; perfectly curved hips, a six-pack stomach, and a thin coat of flesh to cushion the impact of the pumping. As a bonus, she has just enough wild party chick hair to cover the unsightly crows feet. Really. I mean the nerve of bringing those to this show. Oh well. At least she brought a couple of party holes.

The MOUTH leans forward plants a slow wet kiss on the nape of my neck, and gently grabs the mighty Brett sword and guides it in for entry. *T minus 38 minutes to Viktor.*

The Weapon is engaged. We have tone and are locked on. Target is Hot. Repeat. Target is Hot…Must. Pump. Ass. Now.

Brett hears the ewwwppffff sound, a strangled moan signaling we have entry. He wastes no time, and starts pumping away like he's drilling for oil. She purrs and grunts looking at me Eyes Wide Slut. Her anal muscles contract around my schlong like a small fist. Just to be safe, I snag the air freshener from the couch and give a quick toot in the thigh area. If I had a felt fedora hat available, I'd tilt it to my fans, the cocky star of Raiders of the Lost Ass.

The backdoor bandit is very happy now; it feels like I've shot crystal meth into my rod he's so stiff. Sluts, adrenaline and liquor. It makes for a great afternoon.

The MOUTH tilts forward and starts giving me electric kisses, while rubbing the MILF's clit at a feverish pace. This is pretty much as sexy and dirty as it gets. The Holy Trinity of Sleaze. With a view like this, I realize the money shot should be right around the corner. The extra ball light flashes on the Anal 3-sum pinball machine. The MILF breaks out a new repertoire of sex sounds that can only mean one thing. Starting with the deep moans, she slowly climbs into higher and louder squeals, like a Bee Gees chorus would sound if they were masculine. Getting closer, closer….almost there.

- - -

Just at the wrong time, Rasputin starts barking out of his mind, and rips another loud wet one that echoes off the living room wall. The odor is wretched. All kinds of unholy foulness. My eyes start watering, the throat swells, and I start to choke. In serious trouble and holding my breath, I reach for the MILF's blouse and cover my nose to filter the overpowering stench, without missing a pump or beat. Phewwww. That was close. I almost violated sacred sex rule #68b. *Never puke on a pussy.*

The MOUTH is now using both her hands on the MILF, fingers ramming inside, as well as one furiously rubbing the clit. The MILF has got her thumb up The Mouth's ass with one hand, while spraying air freshener with the other. The dog barks get louder and louder; Rasputin fills the air with ominous farting sounding like a sub-machine gun. The MILF whips a pillow at him, and he vanishes.

Brett is a focused and determined pornstar pumping away as fast as I can. I'm holding onto the MILF's tight mudflaps while watching her perky funbags bouncing wildly. I grin to myself seeing a horny fly buzzing her clit. She's getting real close, and I'm holding it waiting for her signal, which I assume to be a Sybil 360 degree twisting head. We may just time it right.

But the distractions only get worse. Suddenly I feel clawing on my back. The frigging dog is barking away in my ear, while slicing his nails into my back and exposed ass. Knifing pains. I swat him off, and he starts spinning around doing the ridiculous chase his own tail lunacy, blasting out more rancid death clouds. The MILF sprays the air freshener directly at him and he sprints out of the room barking. The girls next door are now seriously thumping away at the walls.

Brett the Beast blows the nympho gladiator trumpet with vigor, plunging in and out so hard his balls are heard slapping against her cheeks. The odor has now reached levels of dumpster rank I didn't think were possible, so I clutch the perfumed blouse face mask for dear life. The MILF's head is thrashing side to side, the muscles of her stomach taut, her eyelids heavy as she breaths deep. Her ass contractions increase involuntarily, her face the eyes of ecstasy. Total and utter complete satisfaction, as she starts one final high pitching wailing moan. The Mouth leans forward into a 69 and starts licking her clit. I look down at that cute face and her glasses above those baby blues, and get ready to paint them with a vanilla shake.

As the sex screams hit their loudest point, the baby gets scared and swings her arm, sending the huge Stoli bottle crashing to the floor. She starts wailing loud. Rasputin responds with howling, and rips a heated turbo-blast that can be heard in Siberia. The neighbors scream and pound the walls. Then my cell phone rings. Fuck! It's Viktor giving the 30 minute ETA warning. I'm running out of time, and I still haven't got a nut yet.
It's mayhem in Moscow!

With sweat pouring down my forehead into my blinking eyes, the MILF frantically shoves the Mouth aside. I'm looking directly at the MILF's pussy, right at the moment she comes. Oh God no. She's a major league blaster! This unbelievably thick stream of splooge shoots out of her pussy like a garden hose. The blast is a direct hit off my forehead; the force of impact is a smacking sound  like hitting concrete. The second shot is a facial that splatters into my eyes blinding me. With my jaw open in shock, the third and final blast goes straight in my mouth. Holy Shit. Disgusting!

-   -   -

Instantly, I recoil away in horror from this *Pussy Foul of Epic Proportions*. But since my pants are knotted at my ankles, I completely lose my balance and fall flat on my back, with my legs pinned under me. The landing is violent. As my head slams into the tile floor hard, I hear a ringing thud, as well as some squishing noise. Stunned, it takes several seconds to take in the full effect. Blinking my eyes to regain focus, shock is suspended in disbelief of what happened. I lay there paralyzed, both physically and mentally; a tangled mess of sweat and pussy juices.

My leg is screaming in pain. A thigh muscle is pinched, as my leg is pinned under me in a crooked position. I manage to free my arm from underneath my back, and it kind of slides across the floor in a strange manner....and then my nostrils fill with an overpowering stench; a putrid rotting aroma rivaling the sludge from the bottom of Satan's dumpster. My eyes start watering, and throat swells as I start to choke and dry heave. Holding my breath, I hold my arm up in the air and see it's covered in brown. Instantly, I realize the worst. I roll over and see I've landed in a rank sewage pile of doggie diarrhea.

Like a cage fighter in trouble, I immediately do a body roll and pop up in retreat, spying a window ten feet away. Hopping furiously with pants tangled around my feet, my Viagra rod swings in the breeze, slapping against the stomach. Deeply concerned, The MOUTH kicks back on the couch and starts laughing hysterically. A final lunge lands me on my knees at the base of the window. It gets ripped open, and I start putting dents in the concrete outside with gut wrenching projectile vomit. Violent convulsions and explosions. Spasms and blasts that seem to never end.

It's a sad moment. Four hours of top shelf vodka and a dozen beers get launched. Damn. Just damn. Eventually even some of the green Hairy Balls of Bison from lunch the other day come out and bounce off the ground like golf balls. There's no holding back in this blast. No sir. This is ghastly heaving of chunks from the deep. My stomach feels like I've spent 8 rounds taking body blows from Mike Tyson.

As an added bonus, a wet sensation in the groin signals that while I'm puking I must be peeing on the floor at the same time. You've got to be kidding me! This is a classy moment. Talk about losing control. Finally I put a plug on the vomit by inhaling rapidly while pinching my nose.

Oddly enough, I still feel wet sensations; in fact they're getting worse. What now? Am I kneeling in a puddle of piss? I hear the doorbell, hear more funny sounds, and feel more wet sensations. This can't be good. What the hell is going on? I tilt my head and look under my armpit, and see Rasputin the Mad Crapper is licking my balls! WTF! I also see The Mouth has opened the front door. The two girls from next door are standing there staring at me in shock. I'm on all fours covered in shit, puking out a window while getting my balls licked by a dog.

I jump up quick, smacking my head on the window, rip my body back into the room and take wild swing at the mutt. Rasputin bolts away with an ear-to-ear doggie grin. The girls are howling in laughter pointing. I follow their fingers. I'm still hard. They think Rasputin turns me on! Sometimes Viagra is not your friend.

"Enjoying the performance art girls?"

Their expression was priceless.

"Why you try to hit Rasputin?" one of them asks curiously. "Is his tongue too rough?"

"Nah, I'm afraid of commitment."

"Joo too wild for him. Joo should use a condom. Vee don vant Rasputin to catch anything."

As my shirt and pants are caked in crap, I kick my shoes off, put my wallet in the shoes, peel off the pants and shirt with a bitter beer face, and throw them out the window. Geez. All that doggie licking of my nuts worked up a mighty piss. I drop the boxers next to the shoes, and with head held high with dignity, I limp defiantly with my numb leg through the living room in front of my fans, like a conquering gladiator returning to the king's throne. The porcelain throne that is. As I pass the MILF cleaning up the party puddle, I tell her I desperately need to borrow some clothes and leave. She's a tall bird; she must have something in her closet that fits. *T-minus 21 minutes* to Viktor.

-   -   -

A speed shower removes the damage, and after a healthy shower piss on a defenseless blue rubber duck I'm out in minutes. I push aside the shower curtain, and there's the Mouth with a towel, and the two girls from next door standing in the doorway.

The Mouth introduces me as Rasputin's boyfriend to the girls. I remember one's name was Bubbles. They're a couple of cute butch lesbos, possibly Scandinavian exchange students. Their lean bodies hidden in boring faded rags, with psycho multi-color Gen-X hair. The one looks like it was styled from behind by a runaway lawn weedy, the other looks like she combs her hair with exploding firecrackers. The Mouth hands me the towel. With that contagious dirty grin of hers exposing a perfect row of white, she gets down on her knees.

"I bet them I make joo cum in five minutes."

"Rasputin could do it in under four!" counters Bubbles.

There's always an audience in this house apparently. I like how the Mouth thinks though. With all the excitement, I completely forget I never busted a nut. I look down as the baby faced sex machine teases me with her tongue, licking her way down to the base of the rod. The View was all about her mouth. It's like two red Michelin tubes, soft and wet, teasing and provoking me with every sexy lick of her thirsty tongue. She has beautiful happy dimples accenting her toe curling lips, and a little tiny mole that for some would say adds character, but to me simply says AIM SQUIRT HERE.

Pausing for theatrics, she peers up at me, knowing she owns me. She flashes a mischievous smile at the girls and then me, a smile that could melt Baltic icebergs. Moving slowly back up one last time, her tongue flicks the tip, and then whamm…. she deep throats me. She takes my rod deep with amazing suction, clamping her warm hungry mouth down tighter and tighter with a tongue like a lizard. Her head bobs start slowly on short strokes, and gradually builds, faster and deeper each time, as she slurps and does the hand twisty thing, while cupping and massaging my balls. It's a nerve tingling, nut growling battle for my life. It feels like a boa constrictor has my rod. Damn. I may need a big ice-pack for my balls after this.

Sweat beads on the forehead as my mouth goes suddenly dry, while I hold on tight to her handlebar ears. My heart rate accelerates with each movement, the beat echoing in the throat. The tightening in my nuts builds, as her eyelids get heavier. The neighbors come over and stand at my side for a view of the show's finale. At one point they briefly join in; both sucking on my nipples and fondling my ass. A nice sensation; their dyke tongues no more rough than Rasputin's.

While staring me in the eye, she brings me to the edge three times and then slowly backs off. Then one last time she goes at it, with a look that says *there now, come on baby, don't fight it anymore, let it go*. I notice some tears streaming down her face as she deep throats in

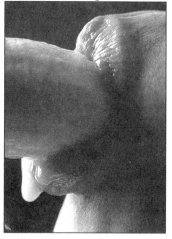

a final Hoover suction flurry, her hand massaging the penis root forcing the blood upwards. My body starts buckling. Standing on my tippytoes, I yank my rod out of her mouth, and the jizz explodes out with the precise aim of a porn fireman. It's a spectacular gusher. The first blast paints her forehead and splashes stripes into her hair; the second shot cakes her *I'm smart* glasses. The third and fourth shots hit the mole spot dead on. The rest are small spurts and splatters, dripping down her chin as she lay there laughing and giving the thumbs up to her fans.

For the final coup d'etat - she gargles, and blows little bubbles.

    She looks up at me and mouths *Thank you* with a wink.
    "Four minutes tops," she brags to her neighbors.
    "That was cool meester. You think you can do that again?" ask the freeloading voyeurs with tight tummies and smart ass grins.
    "Not tonight girls, I'm a bit late already."
    "Come on, Rasputin looks horny."
    Bitches.

    The Mouth slides her fingers across her cheeks and licks them, swallowing the heirs to my throne with a gulp. With a gentle kiss of the head, she reaches her tiny hand out and milks the warm balls, squeezing out one final driblet, sucking it up and then licks her lips clean with a smile. The Mouth is a Pro. With skills like this, she's got a real future in the Moscow business world.

Brett as well is proud of his skills, having stood there on two legs looking important, while scratching his ass and blasting and all. Her fingers run the length of my still-erect Viagra power drill, teasing and tender like. She looks so sexy. So young and beautiful – looking up at me - her glasses and face splattered with a gallon of thick nut. But then again, I guess I'm just a romantic.

- - -

"*Deez I wore when I pregnant and going to da clubs*," says the MILF, appearing from a closet with some clothes draped over her arm. "Sorry, eetz all I have dat fit joo."

Desperately trying to salvage my night from catastrophe, I'm in no position to be choosy. She produces a fluffy pinkish/purple flowery blouse, and a pair of black leather pants with a beaded snake design running ankle to mid-shin.

You've got to be kidding me!

Even if they do fit, I'll look like a fruitcake on the prowl.

What the hell. In a flash, I squeeze my happy ass into the leather, shaking and squirming and jumping up and down till it makes it just high enough above the hips. The package sticks out like I'm packing an anaconda. The blouse is preposterous, yet fits quite well, giving a healthy lift and shapely form to my manly breasts.

"Alrighty then; some fishnets and eye shadow and I'm ready to get my bum violated!"

The girls give me the thumbs up, Rasputin launches an approving toot, and I'm on my way. I race into the living room, snag the wallet out of my shoes and yank out a stack of rubles and hand it to Nympho MILF. I give all my overseas girls money, whether it's expected or not. I like to reward sexual deviancy. I always claim it's for something else when handing them the cash.

"Thanks for the clothes. I'll return them to you tomorrow. Sorry bout the mess."

"Make sure joo return dat deek with da clothes," she winks.

This old bird's a horny one. I see my blue underwear on the floor at the window caked in crap, and get an idea. Snatching the liquor shopping bag off the kitchen table, they're carefully placed inside, bag folded. After some double Vodka shots with Nympho MILF, and some farewell tongue sucking, I open the last Heineken and bolt. The Mouth opens the door. As I exit her apartment, she unexpectedly follows me outside, her beautiful naked teen hardbody exposed for all to see. What a shock! Another horny Russian exhibitionist. She wraps her arms around me and pulls me towards her and licks my face again like a dog.

"Joo remembers me next time in Moscow?"

"Not likely."

She spanks me, and gives me one last kiss.

Soulful. Deep. Like her lover coming home from war. Mmmm. I think I will remember this one. She's something special. A girl who could really do some damage to my heart, if I wasn't such an orgy crazed lunatic with the sex drive of a fifteen year old.

With a mere 9 minutes to the Viktor pickup, I break out into a stiff legged half sprint, as quick as tight leather pants allow, down the tortured patchwork of asphalt and potholes. Fortunately it's less than a half mile to Tverskaya. As I shuffle along in a ker klump ker klump stride towards the home stretch, I see exactly what I was hoping for. The Brit asswipe who tried to trip me is passed out snoring on the sidewalk, his face buried in his filthy hand.

Chippers mate! I brought you your tip!

I gently move his head sideways off his hand, reach into the bag and delicately remove the shit/puke underwear. I place it in his snooze hand. Releasing his slimy dome, it falls into the rank boxers with a chunky sppplatt!

Sweet dreams and sunshine, pumpkin!

A few turns and it's up to Tverskaya, then a hard right, and I'm zooming towards the hotel like its last call. With about 6 blocks to go, Viktor pulls up street side, ahead of schedule. He puts the window down with the shittiest grin on his face.

"Say sailor, did I catch joo at a bad time? It's a bit early to be out cruising for transvestites."

Bastard. I hop in, and quickly spill the story on why I'm wearing the circus outfit, and request a quick pit stop at my hotel to shower and change.

"Brett, why don't joo go out like dat…the girls will love it."

"Not as much as the guys. I look like a walking cluster fluff."

"Nyet! Joo look th-simply fabulous-th."

Viktor valets the DB9 and works the lobby bar for fifteen while I change and meet him downstairs. Tonight we're going roadhouse slumming at the infamous Hungry Duck. It promises to be a fine evening of debauchery at the sleaziest club in all of Moscow.

20.
SPECIAL OLYMPICS DRUNK
IN THE DEN OF SIN

The Hungry Duck

Address: Pushechnaya ul. 9 (next to Kuznetsky Most metro)
Telephone: (495) – 923-6158
Website: http://www.hungryduck.com
(Take Metro: get off at the Kusnetsky Most exit - go up the long escalator and out into the street - turn left and walk 50 meters)

The Hungry Duck is an institution, billed as the wildest bar in the world. Moscow's answer to an Animal House porn fraternity, crammed with hundreds of inebriated topless to butt naked nymphs looking to hook up. It's had write-ups in hundreds of mags – Playboy, Maxim, Penthouse, and Rolling Stone – documentaries filmed by 60 TV stations from around the globe.

Chechen businessmen, four of whom were murdered in Moscow's turf wars, founded this notoriously wild, seedy club in the 1990s. The club's been forcibly shut down and re-opened numerous times, still surviving after infamous battles with the government for lewdness, gunshots, drugs, bribes, gang wars, police extortion, etc. The Hungry Duck has that vibe. That slipping in vomit and having bottles smashed over your head by topless chicks vibe.

Tonight is Ladies Night. From 7- 9 pm, its girls only in the club, pumped with UNLIMITED FREE DRINKS while watching male strippers grind. The chicks are worked up into a panty steaming frenzy, and then the real show begins. Come 9:01 p.m., Brett and the male sex fiends are let in, and are promptly attacked by waves of vodka fueled nympho-whores. On good nights it's 5 to 1 women. A wall to wall carnal pit full of cute, young hammered sluts in a hormonal rage. Female attire is lean and mean. No Prada pullovers, Gucci jeans and Bvlgari watches. Skintight midriffs, miniskirts or low-rider jeans, most of which are usually peeled off during some blasting cheesy disco anthem.

Viktor and I arrive at the iron gates outside the Hungry Duck around 9:05. Hundreds are waiting impatiently in a line that snakes from the Kuznetsky metro station all the way to the front door. Using the metro, most arrive hammered, clawing each other for positioning, chugging vodka flasks as they work their way to the front of the line.

We observe the crowd.

"Viktor, where do these people come from? Are they the rejects from Night of the Living Dead?"

"Da! Joo close, Brett. Deez is Moscow's zoo. Deez are the people who can't get into any upscale club. Dee impulsive reckless youth of public transportation. Industrial style. Dey come in packs and are thick as thieves" as he points out each group hovering in line.

"Halfway house inmates, Moscow State dropouts, mutant criminals, tourist eediots, expats, prostitutes, and cute wide-eyed Lolitas from dee provinces. Trust me Brett; these 100lb girls can drink a 300lb coal miner under dee table."

"Ah, the underworld of society. The best of the worst of the 'new' Russia. My peoples."

The night air is thick and misty, the streets a glistening black under the streetlamps. Drunken Russian voices rise and fall in discord with a sense of urgency, with darting eyes and bodies tense. I find the quivering tension in the air raw and stimulating. It creates the uneasy mood that breeds a fine evening of hunting. Viktor gives me the slash neck move and points to his eyes as we move forward. We speak to know one, and watch each other's back.

- - -

The guard goons here are a sight to behold. Giant monsters with death scowls. Often ex-SpetsNaz (Special Forces), or ex-military commando thugs just aching to dish out pain. Massive chests. Their square domes sprinkled with porcupine spikes in the vintage flathead. Huge shoulders. In fact, their necks are almost bigger around than their tiny heads. What, do they bench with their heads? They make their living on tips. We give zero.

In the street, gangs enforce their evolving territory; bottles are tilted and lines dared to be crossed. Two thugs begin brawling; ham-fisted knuckles slam back and forth into square jaws, bodies flailing on the top of a Volga sedan like Ike and Tina Turner doing Dance with the Stars. In the distance, one of Moscow's finest is extracting his 9th bribe of the evening from a tourist in a rental car. Even riding in taxis you're just as likely to get nailed with the papers and free  rubles requests. The irony is thick. Under communist rule, the streets were safe to drive and walk. After the fall, the iron fist of statism extortion merely transferred over to crooked cops. It's harassment 24/7 unless you have connections here.

As VIP Viktor doesn't do lines, we stroll through. After the crew-cut thugs encourage us to check our heat through the metal detector, we head down a winding dark corridor. Trudging up the stairs, the blasting techno-thumps are overshadowed by the sounds of hundreds of shrieking young women.

Entering the bar, a steam bath of hot air surges in our faces, as a sweaty throng of girls press against us like women fresh out of prison. A scintillating ambience of sweat, vomit, and sex lies thick in the air. Like a penthouse gladiator pit. Ladies are grinding each other in various states of undress in every inch of the club; bodies intertwined on the dance floor, in the booths, in the aisles. Every table, booth and countertop transformed into a dance stage, with beer and slime coating the girls' clothes. We head towards the bar, amidst the crowd chanting for more skin. Girls maul our bodics every step.

Some of these girls are such sluts, I doubt having two legs is a requirement. Like all clubs, there are also skanks, water buffalo, larvae covered goblins, and one-eyed sloths, but they are invisible to my eyes.

On top of the corner bar, a bare-footed hottie with glassy eyes above sharp cheekbones is flashing and dancing seductively in just lace panties, the stud from her pierced navel glinting. At her feet, junior thugs from the outer suburban mafia stand oogling, swinging the arms high with full drafts, showering the dance floor's nearest tenants.

Next to panty girl are classy *dyevs* in hot pants and perilous stilettos, mixing into the action well, topless and swinging their sweaty bras overhead in circles. Intertwined on the main horseshoe runway, two topless province girls stop their kissing and groping long enough to yank each other's panties down. Then they resume mugging down butt naked, oblivious to the crowd.

The bartender hoses them down with the Heineken keg spritzer, and then aims the nozzle over the dance floor, tongues lapping at the spraying brew.

"*This is what I call a target rich environment*" says the Johnson.

-   -   -

Viktor shakes hands with the manager, and snags us a quick round and a waitress. The dance floor is a surging wave of hot dripping flesh, as we struggle to reach a top booth to set up camp and view the spectacle. We are both double fisted with double vodka red bulls as the waitress delivers two pitchers of Heineken. One booth over a plastered teenie is petting the hair on her girlfriend's head which is buried in her lap, her panties at her ankles. Behind us are a row of topless girls standing, singing and dirty dancing to Prince, their bare titties slapping us in the back of our heads.

A plastered skinhead climbs onto the bar to bust a move, his shoes unsteadily plodding on the counter through beer puddles and overturned cups. He's moves to the center island of the oval wooden bar, which is strictly for women. Beers fly in his face from every direction. Blind and inebriated, he slips on broken glass and goes hurtling into the crowd and disappears, knocking into tattooed bulging arms and spilling their drinks during his fall. A throng of crew cut thugs descend; windmill arms and fists go flailing downward in his direction.

A stray punch or two connects in the wrong direction, and then a vicious brawl breaks out between *bandity* gangs, brickheads, and misplaced drunks. Fists flying, knuckles bloodied, teeth go zipping by, gaping bloody cuts in foreheads and swollen eye sockets.

At least 6 other mini-scuffles join in, as the whole section of the bar transforms into a war zone. Not the fake US brawls full of threats and shoves and the two-day stare down. This is instantaneous carnage. Bottles busted over the head, flying bodies, faces smashed with glass mugs and bar stools...and then the doormen enforcers come in. Animals born for intimidation and damage. Instead of breaking it up, they pick up the pace...elbows in eyes, vicious side-thrust jackboot kicks into the kidneys and windpipes. Once the guilty parties hit the hard floor, they get boots to the head and face, enjoying busted noses pointing toward their ear, mangled lips and sliced eyelids, blood splashing everyone's clothes, until the bodies are carted out and tossed headlong into the curb. While dealing out the death blows, the bouncers have the vintage Russian *rovodushnost* look of total indifference, sharing bloodlines of both the Terminator and Rock em Sock em Robots.

High entertainment. First beer pitcher is drained in minutes.

"And so it begins, Viktor." We raise drinks and slam them.

-     -   -

After they clear out the remnants of Rocky XV, the dance floor refills in seconds. In front our booth, a cluster of plastered 50ish US businessmen enter the fray in a circle on the dance floor. Round faced and rosy cheeked, bald and carefree, they unleash an impromptu Full Monty dance routine for their 7 ft. blonde Slavic dates half their age. As their fluid Fred Astaire moves cannot be limited to sharing the dance floor with peasants, a few brave souls climb on top of bar stools and mount tables. Shirts are peeled off. Belly button lint plucked and sniffed. Combovers slicked back.

The dance off begins, with flabby pale tummies sloshing around like Goodyear blimps in a jet stream tailspin. It's a horrid public humiliation moment I hope never ends. I may down the next pitcher in one long chug with skills like this. Our waitress senses our astute appreciation for their graceful ballet flair, and brings two pitchers of Carlsberg in a hurry.

The Slavic babes observe the spectacle with feigned attention in an awkward silence, eyes lowering to re-affirm wallet bulges, and then back at their suitors out of morbid curiosity.

Dexter from the temp agency skips the dance. On his own stealthy mission, he bends over and yanks the cuffs of his shrunken Dockers down to cover the white socks into black loafers. An ambitious over-achiever, he wipes his fogged over spectacles with a devilish gleam in his eye. Displaying a streak of fearlessness that shocks his inner core, he's ready to bag his first Russian pussy. After finishing his prayer to God for this moment, he nervously climbs up and balances precariously on six phone books, introducing himself to a leggy blonde giraffe in stilettos.

"Cool place and stuff, huh?" his chirps in a voice cracking from tenor-to-falsetto, while bobbing his noggin up and down like a coked up parakeet.

"I go to places like this all the time in Boise. Dexter's my name, action's my game" extending his miniature paw, while his taped coke-bottle glasses race down his sweaty nose into his drink.

"Tuhanna" she responds, with an iron vise grip, nearly toppling the Dexter off his swerving perch. He shakes his hand grimacing in pain.

"Wow. You're a strong one.

Tuhanna, huh? Cool name. Ukrainian. I go to Ukrainia all the time and stuff. The Eiffel Tower. The Coliseum. Yepper. Seen all that cool stuff. I'm becoming quite the world traveler. Just last week I took a pilgrimage to see the Tomb of the Unknown Bowler.

Ever seen it?"

...he holds his breath staring at her. Her silence is deafening.

"So, Tuhanna *IS* Ukrainian, right?"

"Dat's my price, eee-diot."

- - -

Up on the stools, several brazen studs of the Corporate Posse break out into some wicked air guitar to Abba's Dancing Queen. Spastic fists are raised high after each power chord, while holding constipated faces of pain and glory. They sneak glances over at their boss, and quickly back off. Don't want to break out the heavy artillery too soon and show up the big man.

Perched high atop his table dance tower, the Pimp Daddy CEO does a condescending head nod, as he prepares to dazzle his employees with skills that are sure to have the stands rumbling. Normally he's a shy Martha's Vineyard WASP, working the cocktail gossip crowd during stuffed-shirt evenings of lawn symphony. Bathed in a gallon of Old Spice, he'll spend hours pouring champagne flutes while power-brokering deals in his royal blue jacket with the chiffon silk-rose in the lapel, his toupee neatly tucked beneath a Newport Yacht Club visor, and his boxers lined with scalding Mexican chili sauce.

Tonight though, he's a sweaty, topless Moscovian gigolo, working his gut and huge-grin dancing like he's channeling Carlton Banks, although his bewildered gaze shows he's not fully recovered from a recent off-balance head butt into the office water cooler.

"Stand back youngins' Let 'ole Silverback show you how to git 'er done!" he bellows with a belly wobbling chortlesnort.

Worthington's hands grasp his sloppy breeder hips, as he grinds a lopsided arc in a slow dip for his star struck Slavic babes. His pants are losing their continual struggle to stay at waist level, but his wingtips...how they shine! He's bustin' it tight. Nailing it old school like he did back in the day at the Sigma Pie grain parties....right up to his fatal attempt at a James Brown high kick and spin. Then he slips and does a slow-mo belly flop off the table, flying head first into the beer and vomit pit with a spectacular splash. It's quite the show, and gives me real hope for my own delusions of grandeur in my Alzheimer's future.

- - -

Second pitcher is guzzled during Worthington's epic dance, while two pair of tall Chivas Regals on ice are chugged to add some style to our sleaze. Underneath a neighboring redwood table, two topless kittens are kissing passionately, hands clawing at each other's stuff. One bops her head too high, and a pitcher of beer wobbles and overturns. A Niagra Falls of suds drips over the table's edge down their bangs and foreheads, while the tongue sucking goes on feverishly.

Overseas, the easiest way to attract women like flies is buying full bottles of liquor. Viktor works a deal with his manager friend for a couple bottles of Tequila. Upon arrival at our table, we transform into irresistibly handsome billionaires, who must be molested and bribed with fresh young skin on every drink. I elbow Viktor and hand him a Viagra, which we swallow with the first Tequila shots of the evening. He breaks out a two gram one hitter vial of pure blow which we tear through in minutes. Like ravenous lions, we do a quick inventory of the available meat, and prepare to pounce.

A dozen provincial Lolitas in advanced states of inebriation circle our table. It's a sex-starved pack of cross-eyed cuties with fresh bodies, funky smells and scattered bad teeth, trying to feed off our goods.
Drunk... Broke...Lack of self-respect.
The perfect formula for true love.
We select the six ripest; nowhere near prime beef. Just a crew of fun, cute, au natural girls destined to get plastered and fingered.
    "Topless if you want body shots."
    Tops get ripped off in half a second.

Rules; one sits on our lap leaning back, her head resting on a shoulder. We pour shots down through the tits. A second girl on her knees licks it up. Basic stuff.

After the first bottle of Tequila shots, their inner slut takes over with raging currents of lesbian debauchery. Now, it's panties only. The rules adjust quickly. After just ten more minutes, body shots require a clit lick first. Throughout the pouring we maul various girls and suck face and dine on nipples, while molesting labias. It's Tequila and exhibitionist chaos. Pray for me Oprah.

About halfway through the second bottle, the ones leaning against us are naked and the girls take turns licking them. The teenies forgot the liquor by now, so Viktor and I take hurried shots before they notice. Two giggling nymphs crawl under the table on their knees, pulling our zippers down with their teeth, begging to give us blowjobs. I stop mine early and leave the table to find our waitress to re-load the bottles and pitchers of beer, as well as take a wicked piss.

After hitting the main horseshoe bar and ordering from the waitress, I look up. Dancing on top of the bar there's an inebriated Lolita with the cutest dirty smile curling her lips. Hair in pigtails, she survives on lollipops and innocence, and a half liter of 150 proof. She makes eye contact, and jumps off the bar into my arms. We make out for thirty seconds until I scrutinize her stuff a bit closer, get bored, and toss her to the wild animals like a discerning beast. Piss alert reaches Def Con 3.

Swiveling to find the head, after a scant three steps a rare upscale scorcher appears alone on the dance floor, surrendering herself to the grinding rhythm of the trance music. Smoking hot stuff. Creamy washboard stomach. Slippery long legs below a tiny schoolgirl skirt, wearing knee-high hippy boots. She's staring at me licking her lips, her green eyes .25BAC rivers of passion, glazed over from 12 beers, 12 shots, and a lack of porn auditions. Brett cynically nods, quite familiar with this tribal eye exchange.

Take me now or lose me forever.

With the crazed scream of an invading Medieval barbarian, I pole vault on my rod into the carnal pit. The Hungry Duck dance floor rivals a swingers club. You can walk up behind any girl and start grinding your dick into her ass while fondling her titties, while the girls do a reach around for your rod and suck face. You can go from dancing nymph to nymph, gyrating and molesting all night, until you choose one to devour in a booth or possibly pump on the club's outside roof. Backing into her with the weapon aligned, Brett starts the slow  booty grind, while singing *Feelings* out of key like a fraternity initiation retard. Her wild, curly hair is soaked, her body an inferno of hormones, sculpted with all the right curves. Her shirt unties, a mildly see-through peach lace bra holds a healthy rack. I kiss her earlobe and nuzzle on her neck. She purrs.

After 20 seconds, she turns with pouty red lipstick lips and heavy-lidded eyes, the swell of her sweaty cleavage pressing against me. The porn music picks up….and then it's full on, with filthy hands mauling her rack, soulful kisses and intense sexual heat. Brett takes her bra off and wears it as a hat. Exposed swollen nipples rise stiff and puckered from her dark aureoles. Gorgeous 38C's stretch freely in the air towards my lips, like the eighth Wonder of the World. Her overheated forehead drips makeup and aqua eye shadow in a Sexy Joker look, her crotch burns against my rod, daring me to take her right there.

Tits. Ass. Lust alert.

She whispers barely audibly in my ear, *I von fuck you now.* I've known her for two minutes. But the body plots against me.

Piss warning raised to Def Con 4.

I signal to her to hold that thought, do the pee pee dance, and race towards the john. Exiting the dance floor, I pass Dexter humping a squat fattie from behind, holding onto her whale gut for dear life with a nerd smirk of bewildered pain. Normally, each day the slightest peer pressure he narrowly escapes a complete nervous breakdown. Tonight, on the slippery floors of the Hungry Duck, he transforms into a virtual sex machine…hunting cattle. His lines are Hemingway poetic, his charisma Bondish majestic, while he dances like fire.

-    -   -

In front of me, an impossibly wasted girl is attempting the Olympian quest of walking twenty feet to the ladies room. She approaches the task with a seriousness of a brain surgeon. Heels are placed down as if walking a tight rope, surging shifts of balance in her swaying shoulders. Each step is taken as though one leg is shorter than the other, and she's forgotten which. About halfway there, Igor, a gorilla with prison tattoos on his fingers gives her a wedgie and then yanks her skirt and panties down; she spins and starts mugging down with him. Her tits flop out of her midriff and into his slobbering mouth in seconds, signaling yet another notch in his date-rape headboard.

Tomorrow afternoon, Igor will wake on a piss soaked mattress with a tampon string wedged in his front teeth, no memory of sex or the girl, forcing him to miss the grand opening of his new critically acclaimed Bestiality flick *"Rambo does Bambi…the little slut wanted it."*

-    -   -

The dreaded Hungry Duck bathroom makes the Exorcist scene seem like a sterile hospital ward. You need fishing waders to navigate the piss and vomit puddles in the men's room, a canoe for the ladies room. All the urinals are taken, but the seas part and a stall opens right as I reach a Def Con 5 piss warning.

I hurdle in over several ankle deep land mines and slam the door. Inside I'm assaulted by a nostril melting inhumane stank. Lining up the target, it takes a twister stance to avoid stray puke piles launched all over the stall. There's one thick gaasspplattt stuck to the wall like epoxy about four foot up, with 3/4ths of a hot dog imbedded in the middle of it. What, did the guy not even bother to chew? The toilet has recently been paid a visit by Mr. Ed with diarrhea. I line up and take one of those two minute fire hose pisses that paint your own pants with spray, if you don't keep a distance. Funny how some pisses are more satisfying than those first high school lays with Peg and Babs. As I'm zipping up, the door opens and it's the hottie from the dance floor. She shuts the door, rips her shirt off and sticks her tongue down my throat, unzipping me.

Come on honey. Slower…and with more feeling.

With my legs spread awkward wide to avoid vomit, I lean back against the wall and get a heartfelt stand up blowjob, while I pat the top of her head reciting 17th century French poems. I observe the hummer in third person and notice she has a lovely smile, infectious personality and pleasant demeanor, in between ssssslurps and slobbers and grunts. Outside the stall, the Sounds of Love are in the air, with flatheads brawling and launching vomit and pissing in the sink. The smell in the stall is a tearjerker. As quick as she started, she pulls the rod out of her mouth announces she has to leave to go pee. A mini-geyser of chunky piss shoots out my dick and goes straight up several feet; we both dodge the waterfall as it lands. Oops. Guess I wasn't quite finished. She laughs, and leaves so the stall so quickly, I never get the chance to offer her a free Brett Tate action figure for her performance. *No respect.*

As I'm leaving the john, I stomp on the floor-mounted toilet flusher and sprint out of the urinal, leaving an exploding cesspool gusher for the next lucky tenant. (yuk, yuk) Next in line is Worthington the CEO swan diver, who instantly cards me, mumbling something about joining him on a yacht of a friend who knows a guy, whose boss he hates. He's in for quite a shock in the john. I must admit he's looking quite spiffy with his Rudolphian red nose and fresh purple starfish bruise on his forehead, rolling Gorbachev style.

As I'm nearing the bathroom exit, there's a *bandity* punk who's Chernobyl wasted, weaving out of control while pissing on the wall. He suddenly passes out flat on his back while pissing, the arc of urine arching five feet high, spraying himself and several guys diving out of the way a bit too late. One of the splashed Politburo thugs opens his fly and starts peeing on the guy's forehead. Several others join in and aim for his mouth. A fourth leans down and picks his wallet.

Mildly curious about my hummer chick, I stroll pass the ladies room but don't see her. During the shortcut through the dance floor, some nasty bearded skank with a horse face that's plastered in zits, tries to wrap her sweaty self around me. Nearly leveling me with her girth, my knees buckle in a hasty retreat. I came. I saw. I ran the fuck away yelping like a wounded coyote.

After this near brush with certain death, I arrive back at Viktor's table to relieve my poor wingman, tragically stranded behind enemy lines. His shirt is off, chest covered with a dozen lipstick kisses, and he's wearing the vintage Viktor shitty-ass grin. He's smothered in liquor and walls of breasts bouncing slick with sweat, gleaming underneath the fluorescent lights. Clearly he's in need of backup. I give him a bump, and being dangerously behind on my drinking, do two shots and two 12oz beer chugs before sitting.

"So, did she swallow?"

He points. A topless Lolita in checkered boxer shorts is passed out on the floor next to our booth with white streaks in her hair.

"Dee guts comes vith dee glory, honey."

I resume the sit down and pour body shots position. Girl leans against me, girl on knees licks pussy, and then I start pouring. Just another day at the office. The girls take turns and are efficient chugging machines. Big, sloppy, sexual entertainment. In just ten minutes, they finish another bottle of Tequila. Suddenly, my arm gets yanked hard.

It's the hummer chick from the bathroom.

"Vie joo leave me? Joo come with me NOW!"

She drags me away from the table and whips me through the upstairs door; outside under the stars on the most famous porn roof in Moscow. Pinning me against the wall, she assaults me with uncontrollable passionate kisses…full of slobber. Looks like I have to take one for the team and do a violent quickie. It's maybe 40 degrees out here on the roof, so this better be quick.

She drops to her knees, spreads her swollen puckered lips and gives me an aggressive pump and suck blowjob. Then she stands and turns her backside to me, my cock pressing against the ass crack peeking out under her skirt. I reach around and stroke her cookie and then yank the skirt to her knees. No panties! Bbbooooiiinnggg! Hard spanks are met with moans. I drop my pants to the top of the hips. She leans back and impales herself on the cock. I still haven't spoken one word to her. With a rush of adrenaline, Brett the Beast starts pummeling her in standup doggie position, her hands firmly against the roof wall. She pushes back into me like a bucking bronco, each thrust more powerful than the one before it. A few soft whimpers escape her lips, in between fuck me harder demands. *Nice.*

Every few minutes hammered couples come staggering outside onto the roof for groping and joints and blow and gawking at the guy pumping the only hottie in the club against the wall. Fortunately the guys glance over and turn back around and go back in the club. Not the girls. An audience builds. I hate audiences.

"Da! Amerikana make fuck with Natasha."

Great. I guess this makes Natasha #7 now. Girls are now standing behind me, kissing each other and palming and pinching my ass with each pump. One is talking dirty Russian nibbling on my right ear, while another is nuzzling on the left side neck. Another girl yanks my pants down to my knees, fondling my bare ass shining in the moonlight.

On the side of the building, a 17th century gargoyle comes to life for 2 seconds and gives me a thumbs up.

'

Out from the door pops one of the girls from our tequila party, dragging some hammered guy in an Iron Maiden t-shirt with slits for eyes. He looks like he's been sleeping in a dumpster for a month. She strokes his mullet lovingly and does a shout out.

"Hey….I know joo. Joo Tequila man."

Brett's not in the mood for reminiscing. Tequila girl and the troll boyfriend are hovering so close to me they're creeping me out. The boyfriend looks in dire of need of me taking him under my wing and petting his skull with a hammer. She hands me a 16 oz beer. I like her immensely and hope we get to reminisce.

The cute teenie with pigtails and braces from on top of the bar comes out and gives me a soul kiss. Then she gets on her knees behind me and kisses my butt while massaging my balls, getting a view of the action between my legs. My right eyebrow dances with curiosity like a Kenyan tent caterpillar, as I casually spread my legs a bit, wondering if she'll execute the Hind-Lick Maneuver. Tequila girl moves to six feet away to play with her homeless stud. I hear giggling while another chick sneaks up and tries to put a finger in my ass. She gets the mosquito swat to move away.

Tequila girl goes to her knees, loses her balance and sprawls out on the ground. She laughs and crawls around aimlessly looking for support, tilting her head to the side like a golden retriever does when he's baffled by something new. Mild concern appears on her guy's face as he checks his vacant crotch. Despite the eerie situation, I keep drilling my girl like a caveman in heat, hoping for a quick ending. She surges forward, and then plunges backward, while peeking over her shoulder at me licking her lips.

Drunk tequila girl crawls up the body of her date like a ladder, yanks his pants down half mast, and attempts a cross-eyed hummer with his wet noodle.

-   -   -

A steady stream of hammered girls venture out on the roof with plastered slanted eyes like pink sores. Front and center is a farm girl with green teeth resembling decayed lima beans, and the healthy beginnings of an Abe Lincoln beard. She's wearing a red-checkered tablecloth shirt and suspenders, and immediately has me wondering who left the gate down on the cattle  truck. I look away, and she sneaks up and leans forward to try and kiss me. When I slap her away, she does a simultaneous hiccup sneeze, sliming my left arm. I recoil in disgust. The moonlight reflects off her pierced tongue ball; it looks clogged with dog hair. Worse yet, she smells like she could be the Mr. Ed from the toilet.

I swat away her second kiss attempt, struggling to keep balance, and politely tell her to take a fucking hike to elephant hell. Natasha screams "harder babee!" every few seconds.

"Wait, I know joo. Joo Tequila guy."

Great. Tequila girl remembers me twice now in 3 minutes. I chug and toss my beer cup, and saddle up with two hands and start pumping Natasha like a demon, her body spasms violently, as she screams out in absolute lust, oblivious of her public sex performance.

My ass gets bit hard. I turn. It's a guy with an overbite that looks like rusted fangs, with his posse of tattooed steroid vampires howling in laughter. With a deer in the headlights look, I squint for a moment, thinking it's a mirage. Each dude is barely 5' 2" tall, and all four of the midgets are wearing some whacked out hat covered in feathers and fluorescent colors, like the Seven Dwarves. Drunk Brits with bad teeth. What a shock! In a pissed silence, I put on some imaginary horse blinders, and go back to concentrating on the ass in front of me. Please make this end.

Four more girls from my Tequila table come out. They see me and wave, and circle me in a fuck huddle. I hate crowds. Two are real cute, and instantly take turns kissing me, asking to be fucked next. Tops come off and my hands are a blur, tweaking and pinching nipples in every direction. One of the girls hands me a tequila shot. I down it. Her friend hands me one. I down it. I love crowds. They  chat with me about who did the most shots, who has the best tits, the best ass, what is the price of tea in China, ….who has the best….

"Fucker me harder babeee, I vant come. You vant me come. Da?"

Oops. I actually forgot I was fucking at the time. Still haven't spoken to her either, which is easily worth three points. One of the tequila girls starts stroking my date's ass, her finger tracing a wide circle around the cinnamon ring. She pours some tequila into the crack, and slides her finger in. Natasha leans back into her hand, legs spasming with greater intensity.

Multiple female hands are palming my ass, while lips are giving me hickeys on both sides of my neck. My girl is definitely getting closer as I feel her pink grip tightening, while the cold air makes my nuts shrink to thimble size. The crowd of girls start chanting "Fuck Amerikana, fuck! Fuck Amerikana Fuck!!"

My ass gets bit again. I refuse to turn and see if it's Dopey, Roidy or Toothy in his green curled up Leprechaun shoes.

Starting to feel a little dizzy.
"I definitely know joo, joo Tequila man."
Not again.

A blitzed Swedish milk-maiden appears, handing me a shot of Stoli, her infinite blue oceans for eyes fixated on my dick plunging in and out. My eyes lock onto her happy rack. Her tits points out like she's hiding traffic cones. I try to toast her and can't reach her shot glass. Her eyes stay fixated on the package, her nipples popping out like GPS antennas.

I say a toast to her titty and click my shot glass against her right nipple and down it.
Clang. Definitely hammered now.

Natasha's ass is pushing hard back into me like a wild colt on crank. The girls behind me push my ass forward in response. Somewhere in the middle is a frightened Johnson, probably beat red like a doggie hard-on, with a bruised purple head. A pair of hands are stroking by thighs, another pair cupping my ass, one is gently massaging my balls, while I feel someone rubbing their bare nipples against my back.

A distinct Armaggedon throat gurgling sound cuts threw the air like an air raid siren. My head snaps right. Plastered girl is going to launch chow on her dude's dick; if she can find it. Natasha's looks back at me with electric-green cat eyes, releasing a low throaty moan, a moan that grows, and grows, and escapes in a long, dirty howling that is half a pained whimpering, and half gasping of pleasure. I feel that warm steel gripping sensation, which is followed by a loud OOOOOoooofffffff!, as she collapses back against me, panting hard and deep, her body shakes and spasms in deep orgasm. I speed drill her like a demon for another half a minute while she bucks and cries and shakes like a mechanical bull on ten. Can't finish. Oh well.

The girls behind launch into a deafening clap and cheer.

A fist raised high with the condescending head tilt, *ladies, please bow to the new Porn King.* But before I can even considered signing autographs and plotting the poses for my Christmas porn calendar, I hear a loud coughing and then gaassppllllaattt . . .

Drunk tequila girl turns her head and launches spew in my direction. Even from six feet away, the trajectory has me immediately thinking *Oh shit, that's going to be real close.* Last second, I pull my rod out and dive to my left, pants at my knees, knocking over half a dozen girls in a human domino. The crowd cushions my fall. Ecstasy turns to astonishment, and then to mild anger. Puke splashes my shoes and pants cuffs, and half the girls' legs. WTF Bitch. My 15 milliseconds of fame has ended. My Johnson is still hard, maybe out of fear.

I look up and Swedish girl's eyes are still locked on it. Her top removed, I pop up and she nearly pokes my eye out with a puffy Swedish nipple.

"You do me now please. *Please?*" with a dreamy look crossing her face. Her hands extend and cup and stroke my rod, her eyelids fluttering closed while she bites her lower lip.

"Sorry honey. I got some drinking to do."

I lean forward and lick her cheek. Admiring her creamy silver dollar sized areolas, I settle for a mild feast, sucking a nipple so hard she stands on her tippy toes.

It takes jumping up and down to get the pants off the hips and up, while the red Viagra weapon is gently parked against the belly button. Eyes zeroing in on the blurry exit, the feet shuffle towards it in a hurry. The applause is thick. I turn and bow, while peeking out from the top of the pants, the Johnson tips his swollen purple cap. Natasha remains bent over huffing and puffing, her hands holding up her body against on the wall. She has a facial expression somewhere between carnal ecstasy and plunging into the abyss. Half a dozen girls douse the puking girl over the head with full beers. More cheers erupt as I get to the door exit. I toast with a final last wave like I'm leaving on a vacation cruise liner; then I turn, and hold a blurry eyed struggle negotiating the doorknob. At last, I stagger back inside the Hungry Duck thirsty and horny. Bartender please.

- - -

A rriving once again at Camp Viktor, I find him elbow deep with a pack of topless teens, an ice cold pitcher of beer, and half a bottle of Tequila left. A fresh new Stoli bottle awaits like a Gladiator peering down from Mt. Everest. Nice. No more interruptions. It's drinking time for the boys. The two warriors forge forward, deep into gluttonous battle, embracing the jaws of hell.

"Very loud on da roof tonight, Brett. Did joo get a look to see vot happening out dere?"

"Front row seats" as I pull up my lowered zipper.

He gives me a bump and leans away, staring back at me with a cynical head tilt. The Stoli label cracks and two shots are poured. No questions, his eyes lock onto a topless blonde slow-dancing below on the dance floor, giving him the cum here babee index finger signal.

"Brett. Women are like elephants. Nice to look at, but I wouldn't want to own one."

"That's easy for you to say. In the US, half the women *are* elephants."

- - -

T he club has picked up it's debauchery to a frenzied pace. So has our drinking. Two shots and two beers are chugged every five minutes. The waitress brings refills upon refills upon refills, as well as a few pitchers of anti-hangover ice water with a skeptical smirk. It's East West teamwork at it's finest. The drinks go down real smooth, and the beer is icy cold. Nice recovery.
Roadhouse slummin' can be a holy event.

Chadworth and his posse of drunks assemble on the dance floor, busting moves like they're auditioning for the short bus ballet. Dexter is hovering right in front of us with a more hideous fat chick than he had before. She looks like Ron Jeremy's ugly sister, staggering drunk with a frozen-vomit waterfall attached to a hairy herpes mole on her chinny chin chin. Bloody hell, she fell out of the ugly tree and hit every branch on the way down. Behind glasses thick as a phone book, his face glows with nerd enthusiasm at having *anything* show interest in him. Back home, the stories of slaying prime Russian pussy will be flow like wine. Yes sirree.

"You're a lucky man, Helen Keller" I yell at him. He takes a hard confused glance at me, and with bulging eyes does the triple take focusing in on his date, his face painted with paranoia. He shrugs and decides he's down with her hot stuff, and kisses her with a gross flat tongue sticking out like he's painting a picket fence. Rock on Dex.

- - -

Some tiny nerd goes scurrying across the floor through puddles of primal muck, crawling under one table to the next like a 3-legged rat running for his life. Seconds later a gigantic bearded monster with fire in his eyes knocks over chairs and tables trying to find him. It takes five bouncers to escort the Andre the Viking out of the club. After five minutes the nerd guy climbs out from under a table thanking the Gods for his luck. From twenty paces away, one of the steroid leprechauns tosses a beer bottle and nails him right in the head. Gong! Give that man a doll.

The kid's got a hell of an arm. No match for Brett Tate in his prime. Back in the day, I was an aspiring pitcher with a wicked fastball, and split-finger curveball that fell off a table like mercury. The scouts pursued me, and at times it looked like a cinch to make into the Bigs. But fate conspired against me. One ill-fated toss in a meaningless game, I blew my shoulder out, and it was over. My career hopes devastated, the shattered arm a fraction of itself.

I had no choice but to quit Little League.

- - -

Glancing across the bar, in every direction topless girls are on tables and chairs and countertops grinding their hips, screaming and making out like it's a porn audition. "OOOHHH. PUSSY CONTROLLL!" blasts through the speakers at deafening levels.

On the main bar, a steady flow of women clamber atop the oval countertop to do an impromptu amateur strip-off. They're in various stages of undressing, dancing amidst toppled shot glasses, puddles of beer, and tossed clothing. Two girls blow off their turns and peel each other's clothes off and lie down on the counter for a drunken Sapphic encounter. In the mosh pit, waves of drunken *bandity* gangsters  howl with approval and surge forward to get a whiff. One sloshed dance contestant rips off all her clothes and holds a handstand for a good ten seconds in front of a screaming crowd, while a posse of degenerates paw at her flopping sweaty titties. She eventually slips and takes a wicked header into the slime pit. The bartender hoses her down with the Heineken keg spritzer.

Heat rises in the club like we're perched on hammocks in a stove, the dance floor below us enveloped in the sensual aroma of beer, sweat and vomit. I'm so hammered, I could swear I see a priest dirty dancing with a sheep in a schoolgirl outfit.
A tip of the hat, Father.

Our party booth has acquired quite the lewd ambience, with semi-naked girls strewn over the chairs while a nude girl is getting licked on top of the table. Two inebriated cross-eyed nymphs in panties have decided its blowjob time  again. Having downed at least 16 beers and 20 shots, I'm bobbing and weaving with the Joker grin in a daze, and not about to argue. We park a topless girl as a barrier between us. The pants are dropped, and we push the top of the heads down.

All hail Pfizer!

Viagra rises to all occasions. I look down in disbelief at the threatening red monster and could swear I've been PhotoShopped.

I'm seeing triple at this point, but it appears the Lolita in the middle is giving some quality head.

"I make joo come if eetz the last thing I do" says the little hottie.

"Famous last words."

A whiskey Viagra dick is a beast to be feared; the girls have got their work cut out for them. During the blowjob we share tales of nymphomaniac decadence, while finishing two more pitchers of Carlsberg, and two nasty Jaegerbombs that go down like lighter fluid, burning the insides with an intense fury.

Towards the end, we're reduced to communicating using a system of clicks and whistles.

All in all, it's another fine evening of carnage and mayhem.

- - -

The stars have aligned, in this frozen moment in time in a subterranean jungle of depravity. Moscow is making its mark on history, like the sweaty concubines off the shores of Mesopotamia in ancient Babylon. Peering down from the watchtower booth into the carnal pit, the two medieval warriors beat their chests, like Bacchanalian guardians presiding over an ancient civilization.

In Man's infinite quests for achievement, in his epoch struggles to divide and conquer, sometimes the answers are so near.

Beer and blowjobs.

While the girls' heads bob up and down, our hunt of the Seven Seas is deemed triumphant. So with chalices raised high, we sway back and forth, and in a deep slurring baritone sing 'ole Viking pirate battle chants.

This is decadent debauchery.

This is Sodom and Gomorrah.

And we are hammered gods.

21.

SLEDGEHAMMER HANGOVER

Fast forward four hours. At 5am, I'm awakened with a jackboot mildly kicking me in the stomach. Oh Oh, it appears Dr. Tate has blacked out somewhere on the globe. A surging drunk headache pummels me like a Wily Coyote Acme anvil dropped from a mile above. Peering through blurry slits for eyes opened an eighth inch, I see a gigantic security guard with a massive oblong head like SpongeBob SquarePants. I recognize it's a Russian outfit…see the hotel logo on his lapel. Oops. It turns out I'm sleeping in my boxers on the floor mat outside my hotel room door.

"Had a little bit to drink last night, sir?"

"No, I had a lot to drink. I'm sleeping in the hall, aren't I?"

"Are you alright?" the guard laughing at me at this point.

"I'm pretty fucking far from alright" slurs the Johnson.

The guard uses his master key on the door, picks me up and steers me back into the room all the way to the bed, which I angle towards with all the grace of a punch drunk Tex Cobb moon-walking. Other than the feeling like I've had a lobotomy, severe head trauma, and gallons of redneck moonshine, I'm raring to go. (merely a flesh wound). Back to sleep.

Waking up at 9am, I vaguely remembering getting a boot in the gut outside my door. I have a bad habit of sleep-walking in the dark trying to find a bathroom, which in this case included opening the hotel door and continue the search down the halls. When I heard the door shut behind me, I came out of the stupor and realized I was screwed, so I just curled up and took a fetal position nap on the floor mat outside the door. Doesn't everyone do that?

As for the end of last night's debacle, the last thing I remember was singing the Viking chants at The Hungry Duck. I can live with that. I've done a lot worse.

-   -   -

At the crack of whenever, the Beast arises guns a blazing. With a buzzing bees noise in the brain like a tenant in an insane asylum, the obsessive fitness junkie attacks the gym for an hour, hurling, kicking and lifting large metal plates up and down like a brain dead Neanderthal caveman. It seemed more appropriate to be in a loin cloth swinging from a vine above naked girls in a mud pit, but…

Gym done, I cab it to Boulevard Ring Park for an 8 mile run, during which my hung over black raccoon eyes frighten more girls than they attract. You mean the Alice Cooper on 'roids look is out this year? Who knew? I head back to the room a down a gallon of ice water and a shower.

Today is a day off for me. Just a few business phone calls with other clients and no clubbing; a little regrouping for a change of pace. After last night's blitzkrieg drunk, I could use a few hours of sobriety. Lying back on the bed with a devilish grin, the mental hard drive re-plays yesterday morning's sex marathon with Aleksandra and Svetlana.

Around 2pm it's time for my favorite afternoon Russian brunch. I call down to Danilova at the front desk for room service.

For lunch, she delivers to my room a Bloody Mary, steak & lobster, and a sloppy blowjob for $75.

A superior attention to service at this fine establishment.

22.
HUNTING PRIVATE LOLITAS –
A ROAD TRIP INTO THE PROVINCES

Moscow's high class nightlife is contagious, an assault on the senses. But for the complete Russian experience, Brett always includes the slice of life that was left behind; the unfortunate other 99% of the country, where socialist realism decays into heroic disappointments. Home to a citizenry with stale vodka breath and rough hands toiling inhumane hours for peanuts, psychologically invested in misery and a black comedy cynicism. Viktor arrives at my hotel looking particularly horrible. It must the company he's been keeping. One glance at each other, and we double over in laughter. A couple of clinically insane liquor sponges with swollen black eyes and hair sticking out frayed brooms.

"Viktor, you look like shit!"

"Da. Coming from joo I consider dat a compliment. Brett, I'm a little fuzzy about how last night at Hungry Duck ended. Joo wouldn't happen to remember da details, like when we left?"

"Details? You mean we have to start worrying about details now?"

"I guess dat's not such a good idea."

"Here's the details. We got drunk and had two blowjobs each from Lolitas without names. One more word out of you and I'm taking that blowjob blanket back from you."

"Joo never gave it to me in the first place."

"You see where your details got you. For the record, I fell asleep on the floor in my boxers in the middle of the hotel."

"Da. I went sleepwalking and peed in my sock drawer."

"And there you have it." Fist bump. Belch. Nut scratch.

Viktor and I commandeer the DB9 through Moscow's outer concentric avenues over the murky Reka Moskva waters (the infamous icy river a sloshed Yeltsin fell in during a press conference and almost died). We map out our road trip into the piss poor provinces through the soul of modern Russia, the decrepit Soviet-era commie apartment blocks, and industrial corporate wastelands To get there from the capital requires a 45-minute drive after we pass the snazzy French Tudor-villa McMansions of the new oligarchs, as well as the Barvikha Luxury Village, an elite shopping complex that boasts not just the spoils of affluence stores like Prada and Gucci, but glitzy Casinos, and Lamborghini, Bentley and Ferraris dealerships.

There's an exposition being held in the village, and the bling and supercars and bodyguards were out in full force. In front of Prada was his/hers Bentley Continental GT convertibles, and roaring nearby a Ferrari Enzo, a Saleen, and the big daddy: a Bugatti Veyron. Ouch.

I feel like a Japanese tourist dork with my camera, so I beg Viktor to get us the hell out of here and steer us towards broke, desperate women immediately. The outrage. The nerve. We must cleanse our souls of these wealthy gaudy people and their ostentatious machines that make us cry like jealous Japanese schoolgirls. So off we go, blasting Judas Priest and slamming Kaufman Premium vodka shots in our welfare cruiser, the lowly Aston Martin DB9.

It's always an unpredictable adventure witnessing the fascinating to bizarre sights of Old Russia. It's an eerie panorama of desolate terrain and time warp reality bites of poverty. It creates a sense of respect for ones own life circumstances. A greater appreciation for being one of the lucky chosen few. More importantly, it allows Brett the Beast to troll high school hopscotch pits with cotton candy tied to his rod, picking off Lolitas who will do anything for a twisted nympho with a bottle of Vodka.

Viktor has a steady squeeze 30 miles out of town, so it works out perfect. He will drive us to her apartment, and then I get to take the Aston Martin out into the 3rd world jungle, and enjoy the fruits of what an exotic sportscar does to a high school girl's panties. Today we've packed the cooler with Carlsberg, Chivas Regal and the crème de la crème, Kaufman Premium Vodka. Expensive stuff, but the best tasting vodka there is. Two beers and a shot every ten minutes is our navigational speed. Just a relaxed cruise between two old compadres, so we take the scenic route to catch up on beeziness, tales of debauchery, and crank out an afternoon buzz.

-    -   -

Fifteen minutes into the trip we come across the first town. It's a second-generation coal district, the life support system of the area's entire populace. Under rolling exhaust clouds with layers of benzene, acid rain and black carbon, both sides of the road are dotted with decrepit steel buildings, leaning storage towers, and skeletal gratings of decayed, burnt silos. Pollution so thick you could cut the air with an ax, while savoring an acidic coal aftertaste.

When the ruble crashed in '98, the factories ran out of money, so rival Mafia gangs battled and seized control of numerous industries, as the provincial cities disintegrated into a rudderless mess. And though Moscow is now resurgent, these parts remain mired in nuclear waste and corruption.

This is a massive Mafia run corporation that violates every known environmental law known to man. Thug capitalism at it's finest, enjoying obscene profits while churning out nuclear waste. If you squint, the silos are perfectly aligned to form a giant middle finger in the air. The stench is so pungent, we put towels over our noses and turn off the AC, otherwise the car will reek nearly as bad as exit 14a on the New Jersey Turnpike.

The company has its own on-site apartment community to keep the elective prisoners in. Sparsely occupied, it houses sullen defeated men, surviving on failed dreams, moonshine and decaying food. The corporate headquarters is a leaning shack surrounded by weeds, next to a chunky multi-colored pond, and a pyramid of rusted tractor rims. The corporation remains defiantly rigid and proud, though, complete with a flagpole raising the tattered company flag with a coat of arms, its symbol a long-range missile crisscrossing a Heineken keg.

The tenants of the dumpster city have all the essentials at the palm of their hand, so they rarely venture off company property; unless it's in a casket. They've got a line of rusted Portapotties without doors, a radioactive waste pond for the aspiring Olympian swimmers, a general store stocked with canned soup, chaw, depends, and enough vodka to fill the Caspian Sea, even a line of shovels in a field of dirt to bury your buddies. From our car, we see two corporate Neanderthals are holding a mock sword fight using severed arms of their fallen comrades.

You're my idol, Cage Man

Happy hour arrives. Forming an orderly line for their liquid coma are toothless, brutally aged men with thick residue-caked hair and reddened faces carved with a superhighway of deep age lines. Like pigs in single file for slaughter. A dour expression and numbness covers their drooping cheeks until the first sip. Same destination every night. Same liquor. Same drunk. It's the company's beloved palace of high culture… The Hairy Armpit.

Arriving drunk from work, they'll proceed to get hallucinatory inebriated, chugging like Nick Nolte hiding in the bathroom at an AA meeting. By early evening, the happy buzz will bring rambling Russian war songs, sung monotone and out of key like they're channeling Jim Morrison. When late night sets in, the sad buzz takes over, when they'll drown their sorrows away with the crusty house special; warm toxic moonshine. The old dependable stuff that fuels the absurd dreams of living to forty-five, grinning with toothy choppers hosting an Armageddon telethon, and the crème de la crème, renting two of the 50ish bearded kettle-bellied *Prostitutki* beached upstairs on the yellow stained sheets.

Although the Hairy Armpit looks like its on fire tonight, we drive on. Raising a toast in the DB9, it's with great regret that Viktor and I pass on the magic at this treasured honey hole.

-    -   -

The highway goes barren, funneling into a single lane curling up and around lanes carved deep into the rust-colored mountaintops. Viktor rips out some astonishing stories of life in the gangster fast lane. I interview for the details and play bartender and feed us liquor, while tearing through his substantial CD collection. Closet classics to cutting edge. All heavy stuff. After howling in astonishment at the find, I pop in Holy Diver from the Dio/Sabbath years.
    "Good call" says Viktor.
    "Let's see what this demon does" feeling speed deprived.
    "Da. Buckle up, Brett."

With hands at 10:00 - 2:00, Viktor's eyes squint and lock onto the challenging terrain. Blistering down long empty stretches like a crazed gazelle, the Aston is a throaty V12 demon with hungry meaty tires gripping the asphalt. As we encounter the unexpected hairpin turns, the heavy British marquee holds tight with its strict 50/50 weight differential, weaving precisely around treacherous potholes. Occasionally, Viktor has to unexpectedly lock them up with split second notice around turns, as we get stuck behind massive dump trucks trailing lung-busting black exhaust trails.

A river iridescent from industry snakes its way through the hilly terrain, illuminated by industrial barges plowing through tires, nuclear chunks and bodies, as they make their way downstream. Along the banks of the multi-colored river are squatters in a significant tent city with companion tree fort condos, home to retired grizzly old pensioners living large on their $140 a month stipend. Underneath the green cloud swells and scavenger seagulls stands a rickety wooden canoe, waiting to accommodate those longing for a honeymoon cruise.

Viktor and I sit in silence, accompanied by the throaty hum of the Aston. Considering the view, words are not necessary. The decayed remnants of communism are gripping realism. The landscape is harsh and gloomy, with scattered leaning huts made of plywood and corrugated metal. Battered men in the distance staring at watches waiting to die, or even worse, waiting for a Cubs World Series win. Profound poverty and hopelessness. How can they ever afford a quality table dance out here?

The topic changes to brighter memories, accompanied by a liquor change out. We shift gears to Chivas Regal on ice, backed with cold Carlsbergs. I spin a few tales from the trenches for Viktor, and then we compare our Bely Medved debauchery tales and rate the current crop of strippers.

-   -   -

The road dips steep like a ski slope, leaving behind elevated greenish smog above the barren wasteland. Beyond the occasional string of oil derricks and pipelines, a desolate building district appears, like filthy building blocks tossed and assembled haphazardly in a tundra of dried industrial waste. It resembles a makeshift military surveillance base, with RKO-style antennas reaching to the stars, set back a half-mile down a dirt road, fronted by a heavily guarded barbwire fence.

Out into the provinces, you leave thug capitalism's legal enterprise zones and enter full-blown illegal central. The richest city in the world, Moscow is supercar heaven. Out here you find hucksters in chop shops selling stolen parts, fixing VINs and titles, illegal street machine kits, and very temporary homes for Ferraris and Lambos in storage garages awaiting transport out of the country. You've got warehouses of stolen Asian electronics goods, massive quantities of counterfeit DVD and computer software for import/export, identity theft specialists, hackers, and more.

Being very risk adverse in foreign countries, only once did I allow Viktor to park and give me the first hand tour. The guards with shaved heads and fanatical expressions accommodated us due to his credentials, but we were stilled monitored every step through the claustrophobic quadrant of hastily assembled warehouses.

After forty minutes, we come upon a small town of Breshnev era communist block apartment buildings, arriving at Viktor's squeeze's apartment. He hops out. After verifying she's there, I give the gentlemanly tip of the cap, and then floor it, fishtailing out of there.

- - -

My destination is a little honey hole of a town I discovered years ago, full of bright eyed schoolgirls who would never dream of leaving town for Moscow, let alone meet an American in a sportscar loaded with enough liquor for an entire cheerleading team.

Aston. Martin. All mine. Brett has a fortunate long history driving sports cars of all eras, speeds, and prices. This particular Aston has a throaty engine that achieves full torque at 1500 rpm, giving you a mid-range pull that's quite imposing. The Johnson screams *"Woohoooo. I feel the need...the need for speed."* The engine doesn't feel like it's even running till you hit 85. Plus, it's got the steering wheel paddle shifters like a Ferrari, to give you those glorious absurd delusions of racing genius. It's like one big dick going screaming down the road.

I take the long way into town, doing an eye-bulging fast cruise through deserted rustic countrysides, before arriving at my destination, a drowsy lakeside town. I'm batting 8 for 8 on trips to this little honey hole, and have no intention of giving up the details of this town, or the route I take.

23.
SCHOOLGIRL THREESOME IN PUBLIC

2:06pm

The Aston steers itself towards the local liquor store, like a GPS magnet pulling me in with a homing device. They actually sell Molson Golden way out here. Amazing. I'm feeling kind of Canadian, *hey,* so I grab a case of Molson Golden Ale and ice and throw it in the backseat cooler.

Liquor Store location: ten blocks from the local high school.

2:11pm

On the sidewalk, the pace picks up quickly. Brett spies two Lolitas skipping and staggering down the road, laughing their hot little asses off. One wears painted on shorts and a midriff. The other is a walking

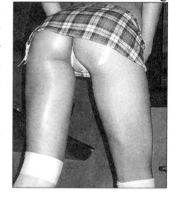

porn movie… white knee socks and black-and-white saddle shoes below a tiny pleated school skirt swishing high on her little ass as she walks, with a tiny glimpse of white cotton panties peeking out every other step.

She's wearing a white midriff taut as a second skin, and over her shoulder is slinging a pink Tweety Bird book bag. Instant Hard-on.

With my tent pants steering the wheel, my heart pounds like apocalyptic thunder. I drool like a lecherous fiend at this barely legal specimen, while palming some hopscotch chalk in the pocket.

Yummy. Two sets of long lean legs a golden brown tan. Even the slightest movements cause flexing muscles to show through her skin. Both Lolitas are perfectly tight and sculptured all the way up to their sweet round young booties. Poverty is good for a young woman's body. I highly encourage it.

As I anxiously watch the girls wobble back and forth down the sidewalk, it's obvious the girls are seriously hammered. Alcohol is good for a young woman's body. I highly encourage it.

Brett never hesitates in these moments. He immediately does a screeching Starsky and Hutch 180 and pulls up along side them with the window down. In these desolate parts, a typical car costs $150, with many families not even owning one. Let's face it; the excitement of the hunt is extinct out here. This is going to be so easy, it isn't even fair. But being the Lolitas are less than half my age, it does provide a token back row trophy for the mantel. Maybe use it as the occasional paperweight on slow nights.

At first glance of the beastly British motorcar and its cocky tenant, the girls scream and sprint over to the window shooting pheromones and lust out of their virgin snatches like a volcanic geyser. I probably should have put the original plastic sheets back over the leathers seats so their pussies don't melt them. The wind picks up a bit, but it's no battle for my dickhead shades and gel-spiked hair. One smirk at the babes, and there's no way in hell these two are doing anything but diving in the car. They beg for a ride. I shake my head no. They plead their case by flashing their titties. I say maybe. They scream and jump up and down like they won a doll at the county fair. Words are spoken, nipples pop out, and the hot little butts dive into the car. The girls' nipples popped out too.

Their midriffs are as wide as an XL sock. Tight enough to highlight the contours of their budding young boobies, high enough to expose flat creamy washboard tummies so lean, they look bulletproof. No cankles here, bustah!

2:15pm
Speaking in decent broken English, it seems these cute little lolitas are played hooky today, and are bloody shitfaced. Brett puts on a Gen-X baseball cap backwards, adjusts the surfer shades, and has a buffet of *Dude-speak* lines to toss out if necessary. I've memorized the names of top Russian pop stars and athletes for this very moment.

I mean like so far the girls were like really stoked I had like beer and like Vodka and stuff. Everything was like so tight! The hotts pucker their lips and start chugging, like the little sluts they hopefully are. For a second there, one of them simulates deep throating a bottle to the other, who giggles and uncrosses her legs, flashing a pink thong. I give them both high-fives, while picturing them with handlebar ears and a flat head.

2:16pm

For some reason they both sat in the backseat. I peek at them through the shades in the rearview mirror. Sasha has long straight blonde hair in a ponytail, shining in the mid-afternoon sun; her face glows like an innocent angel, framed by her golden bangs, ice blue eyes and big dimples when she smiles at me. The schoolgirl next to her is leaning over the center console against me, purring while she looks through the CDs. Tatyana's skin is baby-soft and velvety. Flawless. She has silky blonde hair that runs straight to her ass, a drum-tight eighteen-inch waist with beautiful dancer's thighs.

I try to pick the hottest one. Decisions, decisions. As if it matters. They're both 18ish, in the prime of their uncontrollable lust years. They don't look a day over 14, and have the whole Britney thing going on; heavy makeup, midriffs, multi-colored bracelets, and popping bubblegum. Both are certified, licensed spinners, about 5' tall and a soaking wet 105 pounds. The girls are slamming da Molsons quick, and judging by the slurring, they may already blow a .25BAC. That's not all they're gonna be blowing, but I digress.

2:23pm

The girls haven't done anything but laugh and chug at this point. I've yet to speak. When it's a sure thing, what's the point? Their dirty minds are in overload, way ahead of me. One of them slursssss out:

"Say, you're pretty hot. Can vee like attack joo and stuff?" Tatyana says, as they break out in girrly girl giggles.

"Who wants to go first?"

They both try to climb into the front seat at the same time and butt heads, and start cackling like two drunk girls who just butted heads while trying to climb into the front seat. Sasha pushes Tatyana back and climbs over and claims the first lick. We have a winner.

2:25pm

Without so much as a kiss (the nerve), perched on her knees and leaning over the center console, the pants are unzipped. She eagerly holds the swollen Viagra sword in her hands, staring at it with big doe eyes. Stroking it softly like it may break, she leans forward and purses her lips and starts slurping and bobbing deep like a champ. I gaze down and watch for a while impressed. Instinctively I check the stopwatch and note a nine minute thirty second reading from meet to score. Even more impressive, it took five words to get a public blowjob.

Once again, I wonder how someone so young is so experienced. Tatyana is very jealous, so she takes her cotton panties off and leans between the seats and hangs them from the mirror. I look into the backseat and admire her beautifully nubile, shave pussy and give her a wink. Load gravel noise erupts, I whip back around and I'm almost driving in someone's yard on the wrong side of the road. I carefully ease the car back across the narrow country lanes to avoid any teeth issues, amidst horns and middle fingers. Tatyana in the backseat blurts out "*good sssssave*", and hands me a beer. Brett likes 'em when they come trained, and served up drunk.

2:29pm

Tatyana strikes up a conversation. Like all province Lolitas, she's a talker. Everything in the world is amazing to them. She tells me how exciting like skipping school is, and how like partying and beer and stuff is so like totally awesome. Running her fingers up her long thighs, she says she loves her white knee socks and tiny skirt, as it really shows off the tan she got this summer. It turns her on to drop things and bend over in the school hallway, knowing that the boys die when they get a tiny glimpse of her white cotton panties. She tells me how much she loves masturbating four times a day, what she thinks about while masturbating. She loves talking about her pussy, and fucking, and how great it was to be a girl that every guy wanted to fuck…the whole time she's twirling her hair, blowing bubbles, one time forgetting and sticking her beer bottle through the bubble to drink. I throw out some token stupid high school comments, my favorite Russian artists and pop songs (yuk yuk), and ask her if there's any cool place they like to go like party and stuff and get like naked.

Sasha pops up off my rod and screams "Let's go skinny-dipping!"

"Hell yea!" Tatyana screams back.

A round of high fives. Sasha, resumes her sloppy blowjob with her young eager mouth. Tatyana leans forward and spanks Sasha's size 0 ass real hard.

"No is fair. I no have turn."

Brett is driving about 10mph at this point in disbelief, hands locked at 2 and 10 o'clock. He has no reason to speak. He tilts his head back and slams a full Molson with no hands for the girls in record time. They are like impressed of his bad-ass skills, oblivious of his hidden wrinkles, and the fact he's old enough to be their Dad. He glances at his reflection in the rear view mirror observing the patented smirk. The reflection looks back cross-eyed with a thumbs up nod for my high school performance and reminds me in a decade or so there will be an AARP card in the mail. Fuck you mirror.

2:36pm

Tatyana climbs in the front seat and switches with Sasha, who gives me directions to our swimming hole. It seems like the most normal thing in the world for her to be chit chatting while her girlfriend is blowing me. Good day so far, *hey*.

2:37-47pm

Sasha continues yapping away, but upon hearing and recognizing the location of the river spot, Brett has no reason to listen. The Godsmack volume knob goes up one notch every 15 seconds. Time to start chugging more Molsons before the Teeny Boppers drain the tank.

2:48pm

The Aston arrives at Club Skinny Dip, and the girls are out in a flash…hopping and wiggling and skipping. Brett follows with a load of two six-packs, and a carefully held load that was dangerously close to being launched onto the steering wheel. My blue balls are so tight, they're hovering around mid chest, so I carry the beer on them, while waving to the imaginary camera at a porn audition. Since the wind is blowing due south now, my hair is perfect. The strut is pure alpha fucking male. I gaze into the lens, and sense a porn Oscar coming…

2:49pm
Brett continues on down the riverbank, and notices two farm dudes in suspenders fishing. As he passes them, he does a token Deliverance squeal, and moves on towards the pink taco brigade about 100 yards around the corner from them. The Lolitas are sitting down, looking innocent, mischievous, and horny. The sun glistens off their smooth tan legs, as Brett saunters up with the liquor. Like their stepfather, I squint a peek between their legs, pondering their pussies. I mean at this age, when they're laying down, you could balance a level across their puffy snapper lips and it would never touch the body.

2:52 pm.
Two beers each go down quickly, before I successfully get them to start making out with each other. Though their passion was clearly alcohol, the ritual was enough to get the Johnson to give a minor surge of approval. Secretive whispers in Russia are shared, and suddenly Sasha says "I double dog dare you." Tatyana says "you're on!"

In seconds, the girls are butt naked, exposing amazing puffy nipples, and enough ripe bulging pink it would make a weaker man go instantly blind. Tatyana's snapper has huge lips; they look somewhere between a pink catcher's mitt and a Big Mac.

The girls wade into the river butt naked, giggling and splashing each other across their amazing little one-hand-across asses. Brett coolly observes the Lolita porno visual, and acknowledges their natural beauty by letting loose a violent and reverberating Molson fart. It's strangely pungent, and yet decadently airy. Overall, it was a powerful release, had great sustain, and the healthy staccato pattern shows promising originality.

The judges give it a strong 8.2.

2:58 pm.

Soon the girls are out of view, so Brett immediately shifts into navy seal mode. With the eyes of a trained koochie killa, he scans the river perimeter up and down. Distances are measured; obstacles and dangers are contemplated, until he locks on to a secluded tree in a grassy area about 30 feet away.

Despite incoming AC-130s, swooping helicopters, not to mention parent's curfews, Brett daringly snags the girls' clothes, and moves like a cat to said location, hiding the girls' belongings. He delicately places the remaining Molsons down alongside them, like they're 14th century family crown jewels.

He bows once out of reverence.

For the record, Brett considers, but does not sniff the thongs. He's a professional slut, and respects the code of honor.

3:05pm

On the way back to the beach perch, Brett passes a pack of strippers, strippering the afternoon away, hammered and nude at the river's edge.

"Hey hey big boy, joo cum here and show us jour deek, babee." He fights off a nearly uncontrollable urge to switch orgy teams. Seeing as the girls have an average age of twenty-seven, Brett moves on. He has no time for grannies.

Brett arrives back at his Conqueror post at the shore; he raises a beer and toasts himself. As an added bonus, a fantastic public humiliation moment is about to unfold right in front of my eyes.

3:08pm

The girls' bet was to approach the farm boys and tease them into doing things they would never do. I move around the river bend, and sure enough, I spy them standing in the water butt naked, begging the pork brothers to wade in and get laid. Homer isn't buying it. He'd rather pick his nose and fish, and worship his favorite Hustler at home. My vision was somewhat blurry, but I think his t-shirt said "*Got Vaseline?*"

Elmer, bless his pot-bellied heart, was in pure sucker mode. He throws his pole down, rips his 'spenders and racing striped boxers off in two seconds, and sprints into the water a good 12 feet before falling flat on his face. The girls take off laughing, and sprint back up to Brett the Beast, who's chugging beer as fast as he can, enjoying the show. The sea-nymphs hop out of the water into Brett's arms.

3:12pm
Shivering cold, one girl leans pressed against me in the front, one snuggles in behind me. Elmer finally comes bounding around the

corner, thinking he's getting some. By this time, Brett is French kissing Tatyana, while he successfully fondles both girls in the vintage 6-pack grip *simultaneously*. Nice. A difficulty level of 9.4 in some parts. Sasha is pumping my exposed fishing rod, and moaning loudly. Tatyana starts to say she loves me, so Brett jiggles his fingers madly till her words turn to moans. They'll be none of that.

Back in the river, Elmer is standing there glaring at the spectacle. Looking naked, hairy and stupid, his tragic sense of fat entitlement crashes hard into reality's door. Yepper…once again he's been had.

Brett cheers him up: "Take a picture fat boy, it'll last longer."
Sasha yells at him: "Eet looks just like a penis, only smaller!"
His fishing buddy can be heard howling from 100 yards away.

3:15-4:06pm
Brett walks his naked little teenies over to the trees for a public river orgy. A bootie buffet. Fresh. Sweet. Shaven. Pussies. They definitely passed the taste test. In broad daylight, I strip and saddle up and assume the coochie assassin position behind the Lolita sex kittens. Details are not really necessary. How bad can two teenies be? After saying a prayer to the threesome Gods, I bent them both over doggie

style side by side leaning against a tree. Their tiny athletic asses are beautifully contoured; they look so ripe and perky as I line them up like it's a weekend prison guard fantasy camp. Next half hour I take  turns pumping one than the other, their cute dimpled cheeks provide a perfect grip, their tight skin smacking loudly absorbing the impact, while they like giggle and like moan and like stuff, dude. Two of the strippers come over and stand beside me, watching the public porn show, trying to sell me on their superior skills.

The warm sensation of the teenies smooth tiny pussies is almost indescribable. I haven't felt anything like that in…in…in at least 12 hours. Grunting with caveman slobber dribbling from my lips, I look down and see their coochie's grip is so tight, the pussy lips cling to the shaft like a glove as I pull out. Whimpers and moans fill the air, and after each round of orgasms, they high five and say their patented romantic line; "that was awesome, dude." Eventually their drunk staggering and wobbling around gets annoying; I continue for an extra ten out of a sense of devotion and duty, but eventually stop and save my power for the evening.

4:08-4:12pm
The girls do the giggling bow-legged walk to the car, and it's time to return to their Lolitaville love shack, in the middle of nowhere. The road is lined by weathered wooden houses. Heavily aged *babushkas* sit on sparse patches of grass in the shoulder selling apples, while villagers chop kindling to fire their time-tested samovar kettles.

I pull up with the Aston Martin, which is about as common as seeing a stealth bomber to the residents here. As we park, Sasha is in the back chugging a Molson, while Tatyana is bobbing the rod again, wet and horny. Her cotton panties *and* skirt are on the rear view mirror, while she sucks at a wicked pace. She's lying sideways across the console, so I've got two fingers sliding in the honey hole.

Out of nowhere, she pops up with tears in her eyes, whimpering about how much she misses her boyfriend. It seems he has two years left in prison. How sweet of her to think of him during my blowjob; she must really have special there. At first I didn't know how to react, as she seems so sincere about it. As I'm getting a bit emotional about her love torn heart, I do the only thing that seems appropriate...I pull my fingers out of her pussy, and jam my thumb up her ass and push her head back down. Our Oprah moment over, she resumes bobbing and slurping with an emotional deep suction, while I flash gang signals to a neighbor riding by on a bicycle.

Sasha leans in shotgun, and with a dismissive wave says "Whatever!" Tired of sitting parked in front of their house, I tell them it's time to go inside.

"Let's race!" Sasha announces in a challenge.

"You're on!" screams Tatyana.

They both bolt out the car, giggling and skipping across the yard. About halfway to the house, Tatyana realizes except for her saddle shoes and knee socks, she's naked from the waist down. She breaks out laughing, and kicks it in high gear arriving at the door first winning the race. They disappear inside the house. I look left and see the neighborhood blue balls Dad running his beer across his forehead with a chuckle, while his 300 lb. wife yells at him for watching.

4:24pm
Brett walks across the yard twirling Tatyana's thong and skirt around my finger, and throw a wink to the screeching whale next door. I knock on the screen door for a few minutes. There's no answer. I ring the doorbell, and through the screen I see yet another girl walking towards me. This one is way hotter than the others. Knock dead gorgeous, with beautiful ass-length hair, wearing nothing but panties, bra, thigh high socks, and a pouty smile. She opens the door and grabs me by the hand. Brett says nothing, and very much approves of the sudden turn of events. The babe drags me through the house, while he stares at the treasure trail of blond hairs disappearing down into the crack of her ass. *Bow chicka chicka bow bow.*

4:26pm
She pulls me straight into her room, jumps onto the bed, and has me sit beside her. Brett starts thinking about moving in next door. She is

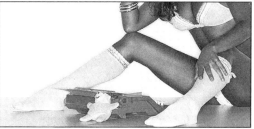

sitting legs spread wide open in front of her is a high school yearbook. "Let me show joo which girls are lesbians." Her tiny fingers whip through the pages, while she pops her bubble gum with pure innocence and hormones. Brett ignores the yearbook, as her panties have crept in so tight, pouting wet lips are plainly discernable. The view is borderline heart attack. Raw cameltoe, with a touch of virgin peach fuzz on the sides. Gulp. Sweat forms on the brow, and suddenly the room goes into soft focus. *Bbooinnnggg.*

4:28pm

She looks up at my crotch, and licks her lips smiling.

"Joo no pay attention. Sit behind me and look over my shoulder."

"Trust me honey, Brett is paying attention." What a little tease.

I slide in behind her. Leaning against her apple-scented hair, I peek over her shoulder down her top. Her tight little body is steaming hot, the baby soft smooth skin is making me dizzy. Her musky scent smells like Jenna Jameson in mid-session. Puffy rock-hard nipples are nearly piercing through her bra. Blowing hot air on her neck, I start nibbling and kissing it. She reaches back and places my hands on her erect nipples, which I roll between thumb and forefinger, causing the healthy rack to swell over the top of the bra, the right side popping out. A crying moan escapes her lips, as a moist stain covers the front of her cotton white panties. Her crotch is radiating so much steam, at any minute flames may shoot clear out of her snapper across the room and melt her pink Barbie boom box. The Johnson is pounding to get out, and using a remote control he opens and closes my zipper in a frenzy, waving a protruding white flag.

4:32pm

"Have you seen Tatyana and Sasha?"

"Da. Dere next door behind da house."

She wiggles her ass backwards, and presses hard against my throbbing rod. For some unknown reason, the hairs on the back of my neck rise, and I feel slightly uncomfortable. That's odd. She thumbs through the pages for a bit, and slowly runs her fingers up my thigh. I ease both shoulder straps down, and both puffy nipples are exposed. In soft-focus slow motion, she gently reaches back and starts stroking my crotch, then slowly unzips me. She pulls it out and strokes it for a bit. Turning around, she pumps and kisses with so much passion she may come with her clothes on. I pull away to slow her down a bit.

Babe: "My daddy would kill you if he found you in my bedroom like this" with a little giggle.
Brett: "A large man, is this daddy of yours?"
Babe: "Da. He played rugby. He 6' 7", 280 pounds."
Brett: "How old are you?"
Babe: "Fifteen."
            (cue video of The Shuttle crashing, trains colliding head on)
A tire screech and car door slam is heard just outside the house.
Babe: *"Oh Oh. Dere's Daddy now."*

OMG! Brett flies out the front door like Carl Lewis, hurdling bushes and jumps in the car, and with white knuckles hauls ass, parking a quarter mile down the street. Against his better judgment, he sneaks through the backyards and winds up behind the neighbor's house. Sasha and Tatyana are found chatting with some cute chick.

4:37pm
   "We've been waiting for joo, vott took joo?" says Tatyana.
   Sasha takes my hand, and I walk arm in arm with the girls into some bedroom in the back of the neighbor's barn. This is getting ridiculous now. All three girls jump onto the bed, and motion for me to come join them.
   "Come on, vee still horny."
   Still shaking from the little sis episode, I ponder the situation. Well, the view doesn't suck, *hey*.

4:42pm
Girl 3 lights up a joint and passes it. As the joint goes around, a Labrador enters the room, his tail wagging furiously. Rover hops onto the bed and starts sniffing Sasha, who quickly pushes him away. Girl 3 laughs, and takes another long hit.
   "Trust me honey, he knows what he's doing" she says with a dirty grin, while petting his head.

Girl 3 gets the joint back, as the Labrador hops up on his hind legs onto the bed. While taking a deep hit with her eyes closed, she slides her shorts and panties off and leans back spreading her legs. Rover starts lapping away while the other girls cover their faces with their hands, but peek through their fingers. WTF! I'm doubled over laughing, but like a bad accident can't stop watching. Around this house you always know why the dog is smiling.

Woof.

Although it's quite the show, after a few minutes I announce I'm leaving. I can't compete with a tongue like that.

Girl 3's doesn't hear me over the loud lapping noise, her eyes flickering closed in a sedated ecstasy. The dog winks at me and waves his paw in front of his nose, a tad pissed at the skunk twat. Sasha waves bye to me while leaning back hitting the joint. Tatyana rises and walks me outside the barn.

"Joo remembers me next time in Moscow?"

"I'm mentally writing you future love letters as we speak."

She laughs, spanks me, and gives me one last Lolita soul kiss.

They say every dog has his day. For a few minutes it was an unbelievable visual, but the Brett Dog knows an exit when he sees it. I turn and leave the girls in their cloud of pot smoke. It would be interesting to watch, but it's seems a bit too risky.

Just what is the consensual age for Labradors in this town?

Moscow Chapel at Poklonnaya Hill

24.
THE OLD COOT FINDS HIS MOJO

C halk up another Provincial Lolita experience in the win column. I reload at the liquor store, and partake in what for me is so exhilarating, so invigorating, it can only be described for me as God's work. Paddle shifters flying, I rip through the abandoned tundra with the DB9, unleashing a white knuckled, death-defying slalom for twenty minutes that would scare an Andretti. Despite being an insane aficionado of sports cars, I rarely drive anymore due to my lifestyle. So these moments are exploited with fury. This may not make sense, but to me I'd rather rent a Gallargo for few hours of navigating the AutoStrada than drive all year. Road rage done, I hit the next town and pick up a rather subdued Viktor, who is waiting for me uncharacteristically outside.

"So Brett, how did she run?"
"She had a shimmy around 120, but it settled down after that."
"Joo got a story to tell me?"
"Same story, different girls."
"Da. For me, different story, different girls."
"Da Fuck Viktor, I thought Kristinka always rocked your world."
"Kristinka does, but she's bleeding. Her cousins were visiting, so she offered them up to me, while she watched. Some seriously sloppy province girls. Different story, different stinka."

My trip concludes tonight, so we revisit the business proposals we've covered, discuss our future business expectations, and set our goals admittedly far beyond what may be possible.

Not the money.
The drinking and the women.

We head back to Moscow to ravish the sweets that lie in every corner of the city. Viktor drops me off in the front of the hotel and heads on. Exiting the car, I notice the old coot is perched on the park bench in a fine pressed tweed jacket, pondering life while looking off into the distance. Strange…he's without his  pigeons or a young dyev to keep him company. He surveys me from and distance and signals me to come over and pay my respects.

So I wonder to myself…why is the old man so curious about me? Maybe I'm the ghost of Sex Addicts past for him. Was he voracious gigolo who lost his edge and is now a haunted shadow of himself? Has alcohol taken the place of mischievous hunts, leaving him a sympathetic mutant, a part of him proud of his past female conquests, a part sickened with guilt thrust upon him by beefy feminists? Or is he just a fucking old coot as hard as his arteries with his decadent-nose-in-my-face?

"I say old chap, it appears by your ruffled attire that you've experienced a bit of a tussle. I thought you were only going out for a meal. Did you encounter a tad more than you expected?"

"The meal went as planned. Quite delicious, actually. I must inform you that I will be leaving Moscow this evening on a red eye flight."

"Do tell! My captain's chair will become quite tedious without your parade of ladies."

"Judging by your healthy flock of nubile *dyevs*, I think you'll manage. I believe you've owed me a story for a few days now. Exactly what happened with the women who's face is inside the locket around your neck. You're hiding more than you admit."

He issues a heavy sigh, and takes a long puff from his Chesterfield pipe shaking his thick gray locks. Several brusque ahems, followed by a lengthy pause. He squints at me intensely. I nod my head up and down without speaking, looking down and away. Sitting up straight, he crosses his leg, tapping his cane on the pavement below.

-    -   -

"Oh, what the hell. My first trip to Moscow as a younger man, I was easily impressionable. I walked the faded asphalt inside the Red Square between the cathedrals, listening to strangers piss about their local color and sounds. I heard the stories from the long-winded soldiers of wars past; watched their eyes sparkled as they re-lived the Great Bear's tanks crossing the Red Square, flexing Russia's mighty hand towards inbound German brigades.

And there she was.

Like a whisper in the wind, flittering by me in the shadows with raw innocence and sensual purity.

I fell completely in love with this woman.

It began with her following me around trying to sell me silver necklace medallions, and ended up I was the one following her around, just trying sneak peaks at her. It was a maddening cold winter, with bone chilling winter gales and blistering snowfall. She was all buckled up. I never saw anything except her eyes.

And her pride masking her pain.

Those eyes - you could dive right into them and be lost forever."

-    -   -

Brett nods with a feigned awe, entering that realm when old people start boring you to tears, as in 15 seconds. Looks like I made a bad call. This may turn out to be a painful experience.

-    -

"We went to a café and sipped cappuccinos. In pathetic broken dialect, I shared vague nothings, bored of my privileged life, while beaming hormones. She shared a story of her grandmother bouncing her on her knee as a child under a poplar tree, reminiscing about her ancestor's from the 16th century on, giving thanks to God each morning under that very same tree, before plowing the fields in sub zero temperatures. She dreams warm feelings of her lineage and of that Poplar tree, but can't remember where it is. Yet it is a part of her." He leans back and nervously lights his shaking pipe held choked in his weathered hands, attempting to regain momentum.

- - -

Brett shares a smile and utters fake cackles and guffaws, while fighting the urge to pee on the old coot's shoes. A hand covers my mouth. There's no reason to let snoring stop a good rambling Alzheimer's tale.

- - -

"In no time, we had a torrid relationship going, seeing as I had a warm bed, generous funds, and naïve romantic intentions. I surrendered my soul to her unconditionally. Oh my, how my knees went weak with her sculpted body and untamed blonde hair. She had fire in her blood, and flames in her pants. She was perfect" he says with a huge sigh and a schoolboy grin.

- - -

My beer has gone warm, and a thick gray Gandalf beard has morphed on my chin. If I don't break free soon from old leather face's *Tales from the Crypt*, I'll be crapping my pants and dreaming of getting a granny gum-job.

- - -

"One crisp November eve, I took her inside St. Basil's Cathedral and we took meaningless photos. She was illuminated with a timeless glow, having been too nervous to visit the magnificent landmark alone, despite it being so much a part of her heritage. On Xmas, she surprised me with this handmade necklace medallion with her picture inside. It warmed me deeply, like my first Boy Scout fire. I've never seen her since that day" shaking his head looking down and away.

- - -

To avoid the constant bouts of unconsciousness the sullen prose has inflicted upon me, I nod my head like a parakeet while slapping my face silly. The Johnson cries for oxygen, yelping"...*here's an idea. When you're telling a story, have a point. It makes it so much more interesting to the listener.*"

"I shine the silver daily, and still rub my fingers underneath its smooth belly like it's her cute little tummy. But it's become a cold artifact, joined by my bitter heart over time. There just hasn't been another girl to replace her. It would seem somehow dishonorable of me to even consider someone else. Frankly, I've got more money than God, but I can't even buy an erection I'm so obsessed with her."

\-   \-   \-

Pondering if boring drivel is actually a legitimate language, and not just a technique to punish me with a psychotic glee, Brett uses the break to urgently call 911 for a defibrillator to keep me alive. Despite a valiant effort, I may go down for the count before the tale unfolds. The careflight helicopter hovers over head with a sense of urgency. This could be a coffin buster.

\-   \-   \-

"I'm never lonely", he continues with a renewed corpse vigor.

"The Russians are my people now. The locals stop by for a listen once in a while. I've become a local character. I amuse them. They amuse me. They pretend to like my old repeated stories, even pretend they understand all the English. But not a day goes by I don't think about her" brushing some lint off his suit lapel with a heavy sigh.

\-   \-   \-

Brett puts the gun pressed against his forehead down with a sense of relief. The crusty old bugger may be done.

"Quite a tale, Scrappy. But you gotta let her go, man. Let her go. Life's too short. I must head inside for a previous engagement. Enjoy the evening…oh, and one more thing."

"What's that son?"

"You've got that look. I hope you find it." I spin and hustle for the hotel door before he starts up again. Yikes. Old and can't get it up. Nice combo.

\-   \-   \-

Heading upstairs, I call my old clients for a chat and farewell, and decide to make one more bootie call before packing and hitting the lobby bar. My flight isn't for six hours. Dialing her number from a napkin on the table, she answers it once again on the first ring. "That thing still warm?"

"Da! Eetz steaming. Joo ready for another taste test?"

"Da. My flight isn't for hours. Want to come over my hotel and get spanked? I have to give you back your Mom's hippy chick clothes."

"I'll be right there." I give the Mouth directions and pack my stuff and shower.

The Mouth arrives in fifteen minutes with a naughty horny glow painting her face. The second  time with her proves to be no less than unbelievable. Not even Walt Disney has made a better ride. It's feel like I've gone ten rounds with a cagefighter I'm so exhausted. ..when all the sudden I come up with a brilliant idea.

After running it by The Mouth, she makes a phone call which seals the deal. We head back downstairs. She waits for the evil plot instructions at the lobby bar. I bring two Carlsbergs outside and check in with the old coot, who is still without his pigeons and looking a bit sad.

"You're still not looking healthy, pops."

"Not sure if it's mental or physical, actually."

"I've brought you my own time tested cure. Here's a multi-vitamin with a Carlsberg, surely a great head start for your comeback" handing him a Carlsberg and *a 100mg Viagra*. (unknown to him).

"A splendid idea....cheers."

"I must hit the lobby bar for a bit. Hold that thought."

I head back inside and hang out with The Mouth for a drink. We both go back outside after twenty minutes. A prominent reddish tint and a touch of sweat coats the Old Coot's forehead. It looks like we're right on schedule.

"I'd like you to meet my future ex-fiancee, pops."

She shakes his hand and stands directly in front of him in her tiny black miniskirt.

"The pleasure is all mine. And what a vivacious *dyev* you are."

"Ivana is quite the athlete. Show Broderick how strong your legs are" with a big wink to the Mouth. She giggles and lifts up her skirt mid-waist, flexing her legs with a roguish grin. Oops. No panties.

"Bet you haven't seen strong legs like that in a while, Pops."

"Son, I don't know if I've ever seen anything as beautiful as that" with a mystified twinkle in his eyes.

The Mouth keeps flexing her legs in various positions like she's in a Ms. Fitness pageant, while keeping her cookie in plain view. Standing behind the Old Coot, I reach around and touch the medallion on his neck.

"Mind if I see the face of that woman in your locket again?"

"What woman….oh that silly thing." He hands it to me without breaking his laser lock on the Mouth's coochie. An arm goes around my waist from behind me. I turn and we share a nod. Nympho MILF walks out in front of the Old Coot alongside the Mouth….and lifts her skirt. Oops. No panties. *Bow chicka chicka bow bow.*

I walk over in front of the old geezer and stand next to the MILF, holding the open locket exposing the female face next to hers.

"Why could this be your long lost woman from the locket?"

He stands with a raging tent pole. Viagra is his new friend.

"Close enough" he says with a gigantic schoolboy grin. He shuffles forward and wraps his arms around the MILF in a bear hug. She plants a wet kiss on his crusty lips. (She loves money).

"Brett, this may be the greatest day of my life!"

I shake his hand; inside my palm is a vial of Viagra. He reads the label, winks at me, and quietly puts it in his pocket.

A horn goes off in the distance. Over at the valet stand, Viktor pops out of Dmitry's limo, waiting to take me to the airport.

"Brett, we launch in twenty-five. I'll be inside the car" he says, waving his King Viktor BJ blanket at me with a shitty grin.

-   -   -

I go upstairs for my luggage, and the Mouth sneaks in beside me as I enter the hotel room. What am I, just a piece of meat? Without a word, she shuts the door and gets down on her knees. Her eyes locked on my crotch as she unzips me, her mind in a sensual hypnotic daze, her lips pursed and ready to suck a volleyball through a garden hose.

She performs her unbelievable Hoover magic again, reducing me to a trembling mess in less than five minutes. Another toe curling, nut growling, heavy panting masterpiece.

Damn girl.

Just to be a good sport, I return the favor and open the room window curtains and press her up naked against the glass for a stand-up doggie that can be plainly seen by everyone on the street. The Nympho MILF and the old coot wave and resume kissing.

As we leave the hotel room, she pushes me against the door and smothers me one last kiss.

Slow. Sensual. Like old lovers. Ouch. I'm going to remember this one. She's something special. A girl could really do some damage to my heart, if I wasn't such a blitzed sexual deviant and a cold hearted prick.

- - -

B ack downstairs, we say our goodbyes as I settle up the bill at the front desk. Moving outside, when I walk to within ten yards of the limo, both back doors open and four naked nymphs hop out and run to me. While Viktor puts my luggage in the trunk, all four girls kiss me and molest me like a soldier coming home from war. The valet guys face looks like he's seen a ghost, while he quietly sheds a gallon of alligator tears. I look back at the door entrance, and the hotel front desk girls are there blowing me a kiss, without the slightest sign of jealousy.

What a day. What a city. What a rack on that perky little Danilova.

I look right. The MILF is sucking face with Old Daddy Big Bucks, and looks quite happy snuggling up to his Old Spice, moth balls and depends scent. They wave as they walk together holding hands towards the hotel. The Old Coot pauses, and spins towards me with a bow, tipping his crisp Gatsby pancake cap with a big huge grin.

Our vastly divergent paths in life have reached an identical hedonistic destination. Mission Accomplished.

My work is done here.

The girls and I get into the limo. It's a new batch tonight, all curves and smiling lust. And bombed. And barely legal Lolitas. Stroking each other in heat, fingertips run softly over the swell of a hip, a tongue tracing the curve of a nipple. By the time we edge 50 yards from the hotel driveway, Viktor and I are already hiding behind our Coat of Arms BJ Blankets, listening to a chorus of slurps and giggles. The traffic is horrible as usual, but there's plenty of time before my flight. Viktor elbows me. Out his window to my right, a Volga taxi passes us with a mildly faded *Cum see me at anal-granny-fucker.com* bumper sticker, a victim from a previous trip of mine. It's the little things.

The coat of arms blankets were busy for the whole airport ride. Dmitry calls in by cell to say goodbye, the whirring of helicopter blades loudly humming in the background. He's tragically found himself bombed and elbow deep with strippers, about to land on his out-of-town castle's helipad and hit the Arbat casinos.

Standing outside the limo at the airport, my wingman and I look at each other shaking our heads and bust up laughing. Two pussy mercenaries whose guns are still smoking from their exceedingly lecherous week of battles. The debauchery has set new highs and new lows at the same time. Grasping the company flag, we pound our chest plates, click swords and raise them high, unleashing one final gladiator scream to the Gods of Testosterone. The legends and tales will be inscribed in the sacred tablets and sealed in the Bacchanalian vaults, for future generations to ponder in awe and disgust.

"Viktor you magnificent bastard. I'm not going to stand here and blow sunshine up your ass. Let's just say it was a nice addition to an obscene history of binge-drinking nymphomania and debauchery."

He gives me a bump and points his finger gun with a wink.

"You were good kid. Real good" says the Johnson.

. . . and in the words of General MacArthur. *I Shall Return!*